Neurological Reparative Therapy

A Roadmap to Healing, Resiliency and Well-Being

Dave Ziegler, Ph.D.
Executive Director,
Jasper Mountain,
Jasper, Oregon

Jasper Mountain
37875 Jasper-Lowell Road
Jasper, OR 97438-9704

E-Mail: davez@jaspermountain.org
Website: www.jaspermountain.org

International Standard Book Number: 978-0-9821214-7-4
Library of Congress Control Number: 2011936921

Printed and bound in the United States of America

JASPER MOUNTAIN
Hope for Children & Families

This volume is dedicated to

all those who desire to have a deeper understanding

of traumatized children and adults,

and who put this understanding into action to help others.

You are the real heroes of our society.

Acknowledgments

It has been a joy to work over the last three decades with the devoted people who compose the Jasper Mountain family. It has always been the best elements of a family—coming together to grow and learn and all the while supporting each other in the challenges life presents. And there has never been a shortage of challenges. I learned from my father that teamwork can make even the most challenging job a growth producing and worthwhile experience. He returned from World War II feeling like he had been a contributing member of one of the largest teams ever assembled on the planet. He did his part, the goal was reached, and he learned many life lessons from this challenge that stayed with him the rest of his life. Our challenges at Jasper Mountain are much different than the hostile skies over Nazi Germany, but our challenges are very real. I could not have done my part, or others done theirs, if we had not had the amazing team we have had over these years. For the children and families that were helped, the credit goes to the synergy of our collective efforts and the treatment family we became along the way. I want to thank all the thousands of members of that family over the years. Some have been a part of the family from day one and others for only a short time, but it has taken everyone's contribution and I want to express my appreciation to everyone for playing their part.

In a special way I want to thank the men and women of our Board of Directors over the history of the organization. In large and small ways the Board has played a critically important role in our successes. Many challenges that threatened the very existence of Jasper Mountain were directly met by the Board and they never compromised their values for expediency. The support the Board has provided from the beginning of the organization has exceeded any Board I have ever been associated with. Every current and former Board member can take pride in their contribution to our overall accomplishments and what we have become. Because this book includes the story of Jasper Mountain, I want to mention the Board members, beginning with our Board presidents over the years: Larry Hill, Mike Kelly, Frank Papagni, Steve Cole, Debra Eisert, Chuck Davis, and Barb Lucas. Other Board members include: Linda Beach, Gary Buss, Rob Morris, Gene Heinle, Randy Nawalaniec, Parke Blundon, Nji Nnamani, and Sharon Stanfield. Former members include: Steve Egeter, Gretchen Teeple, Bill Barrett, Ron LeBlanc, Shelly Kurtz-Jack, Becky Higgins, Rick Dancer, Peter Sherman, Dan Hill, Dave Ellingson, Amy Silverberg, Walt Cissel, Brent Andersen, Carol Miller, John Lively, Michael Warren, and Romaine Straub.

The hands-on work has required a long list of dedicated professionals that cannot all be named here. I will acknowledge the current Management Team of Judy Littlebury, Kiva Michels, Don Landauer and Jeff Huston and our staff advisors Janet Gielow and Julie Engel. Dedicated staff who have been with the team for more than 10 years include: Linda Christensen, Kelli Stonelake, Gail Keller, Erin Littlebury, Linda Leckington, Dave Rooney, Karla Thomsen, Chris Turner, Carol Anderson, Melanie Bernabe, Eden Huston, Mary Gross, Barbara Gentry, Andy Tyler, Kristi Slaughter, Victor DiMino, Sue Baker, Tim Ellenberger, Cory Taylor, and Terri Jones. Former staff with us for more than a decade include: Dan Silver, Valerie Isenberg, Craig Steinberg, Carmen Trimble, Dan Vink, Patty Earl and Gabe Hankins.

A number of editors have helped in this project including: Jane Carter, Ryan Adams, Kiva Michels, Linda Christensen, Beau Garner, Michelle Perin, Judy Littlebury, and Julie Engel. Several therapists contributed examples throughout the book of their direct experience with clients using the NRT model, these therapists were Renee Villanueva, Marta Prato, Femeke Britschgi Cabernard, Shannon Sell, Alex Hager, and Jeff Huston.

Contents

Chapter 3

The Foundation of Neurological Reparative Therapy 29

Chapter 4

The Five Goals of Neurological Reparative Therapy 65

Chapter 5

The Five Procedural Steps of Neurological Reparative Therapy

Chapter 6

How Neurological Reparative Therapy Informs Interventions

Chapter 7

Neurological Reparative Therapy in Practice —
Case Example of Improving Neuro-Integration

Chapter 8

Neurological Reparative Therapy Intervention
Protocol in Action — Case Example

Chapter 9

Understanding the Real Problem can Lead to Counterintuitive Interventions — Case Example

Chapter 10

The Jasper Mountain Story — Innovation Coming from Direct Experience

Foreword

One of my favorite professional pastimes is to read everything I can find about the human brain. Fortunately, I live at a time when there is a great deal of information available on the brain. Add this to the fact that there has never been a better time to find out the intricate workings of the most complex organic substance in the known universe—the human brain. Since I read a lot, I have opinions as to what I like and dislike about the writing of others. One of the best parts of writing my own books is the ability to provide to the reader what I personally find to be of the most interest and most practically useful. If at any point in the following pages I fail to excite you to the degree that I am excited about the human brain, then I have failed. There is absolutely nothing I can think of that is more interesting, more amazing, and more important for us to understand and appreciate than this most precious of gifts that every living person possesses. In the same way, if I do not give you a clear sense of how to practically use any of the approaches covered, then I have missed the mark. I want the reader to experience the excitement and the application of using the ideas we will be exploring.

The more I study and understand the brain, the larger the role it plays in the psychological treatment that I direct at Jasper Mountain in the Cascade Mountains of Oregon. We have frequent guests come to our treatment center from all over the world and they tell us there is nothing quite like our program anywhere. Over the three decades we have labored to understand the needs of traumatized and damaged children, we have perfected our ability to help these children and their families. Due to a convergence of factors, we can now more clearly define exactly what we do at Jasper Mountain and why even we are amazed by the effective outcomes the treatment produces.

This book is an answer to the question we are frequently asked at Jasper Mountain, "What do you do that can be replicated in other settings?" It is true that a unique set of circumstances can be found at Jasper Mountain and some of what comes together in this healing village may not be easily replicated. Despite this, Jasper Mountain will be the focus of one of the following chapters. This is not because a franchise of Jasper Mountains in other locations is being proposed. The reason one chapter will highlight Jasper Mountain is because it is a living example of how the principles outlined in this book can be practically implemented, resulting in long-term change in even the most challenging children. While not all that can be found at Jasper Mountain can be replicated, much of what constitutes the active ingredients of change can be integrated into other settings, such as the focus on brain change.

The convergence of factors I refer to include the explosion of information from brain research that has been available particularly over the last fifteen years. While this information has become available in large part due to the advancements in technology, Jasper Mountain has struggled daily to help the most damaged children our society faces. In this pursuit of what often feels like an impossible challenge, there is a daily urgency to leave no stone unturned to find a better way to help our damaged children. In a sense, it is like parents who would do anything to help their ailing child and patiently waiting for answers to come from somewhere is not an option. The treatment at Jasper Mountain is very much like this because we are parents, every child we treat is very much our child, and we have never patiently waited for answers to come from somewhere else. Our children are ailing and without immediate and effective help, their futures are very much at risk in respect to their psychological as well as mental and spiritual health.

This is part of the true story of Jasper Mountain, a place that from the beginning pursued the most damaged children and accepted the challenge of finding answers and becoming the road less traveled that can lead to a better future and a full life. Our children deserve no less. However, our challenges include not only children who were unspeakably harmed by adults through abuse and neglect, but also the damage the problematic early lives caused to the child's sense of self and hope and optimism for the future. Our challenge has never been to show children the way to a better life; if only it were this easy. What we have had to do is override the perceptual distortions, the negative inner working models, and the instinctive fight or flight mechanisms that produce every thought, every emotion, every decision and every behavior. It is precisely these distortions that produce the inability to cope and result in mental health disorders. Describing our task differently, we have to take on the challenge of showing a child the way to a better life when all the child sees is a trap they must avoid at all costs. In other words, we have to first take on the damaged neurological perceptual and processing issues within the child's brain before they will even be willing to listen to us describe a different road for them to travel to reach their goals and dreams.

Our system of care is too often focused on the immediate: how to reduce a child's violence right now, where to find a place that can handle a child for tonight, and how do we get through the school term with the teacher and the classroom in one piece. However, while the tyranny of the immediate must be addressed, we cannot lose sight of the long-term view. We must help the child learn today the skills he or she will need ten and twenty years from today. If we do not have this long-term perspective, we have not provided the child what they will need for the life we want them to have access to.

Jasper Mountain has avoided being wedded to any particular model, allowing its staff to see the challenges of these damaged children with fresh eyes and only one priority to any particular approach—does this intervention work with this child? Combining a treatment center with some of the most damaged children in our system of care at the same time new insights into the brain were coming out of technology and scientific research has produced a greenhouse of trial and error to implement the most current information concerning the mechanisms of the human brain.

Therefore, from a small program in the rural mountains of Oregon has come a new model to understand and help children, and it is based upon repairing the past and opening a door to the future. In a way this seemingly unlikely scenario makes sense; where else would one expect to find innovation if not in the front lines of mental health work with the urgency to find answers every day. Jasper Mountain does not claim any special insight or expertise in offering this new model to others. Perhaps it is most accurate to say that necessity has once again been the mother of invention, or should I say innovation. In offering this model, every effort will be made to put our current understanding of the brain in proper context, including the last chapter of this book. We do not yet know what we do not know and, therefore, we must approach impacting the human brain with a fair amount of humility and caution. By the time this book makes it to the hands of the reader, changes will have already been made in the model due to new insights into the brain and practical experiences of testing the model in daily real world situations. The best information comes from *in vivo* or real life situations. Some of the greatest advancements in medical trauma care have come from wartime combat. It makes sense that some of the most significant advancements in psychological trauma work would also come from the trenches of intensive mental health treatment.

Do not allow yourself to get discouraged by any lack of clarity or unintended confusion you may find in the book. There is more information available for any concept that I may have failed to clearly explain. While the brain is clearly the most complex of any organic or, for that matter, mechanical structure, complexity does not equate to unintelligible. We can and must use our brain to understand our brain, which is the fundamental difference between humans and the rest of creation, we can contemplate ourselves. With such an ability comes the responsibility to define our experience rather than passively be impacted by all that surrounds us. With the ability to understand the human brain also comes the responsibility to assist each other, particularly our children, in optimizing our ability to perceive, alter, and to heal the inevitable harm that life hands to every human being. It is in this spirit of self-understanding and assisting others that this book is offered.

The term plasticity is frequently used in neuroscience. The term actually goes back more than a century in its use. The term is meant to convey how changeable the brain is throughout life. However, I do not find this the best of terms to convey the desired meaning. While the word plastic fits to convey how the brain can be molded or shaped into a certain form, it fails to convey how this process is continual. The term malleability has been suggested as an alternative, but this is not a common term for many people. Throughout this book I will use what I consider to be a better term to convey both the shaping and forming of the brain as well as the continual process of the brain changing with each experience and being reformed throughout life. The term used here is neurotransformation.

This book is presented in a logical or developmental order. It begins in Chapter 1 with the reason a new model developed out of necessity to incorporate expanding research in related areas of psychology and brain science. In Chapter 2 the new model is explained first as to what it is and what is isn't. This chapter stresses that Neurological Reparative Therapy (NRT) can be incorporated into a wide variety of treatment techniques. Chapter 3 provides some of the main areas of research that form the empirical and literature basis for this new model. The emphasis on evidence-based practices can at times be misleading since some techniques are much more prone to empirical study than others. In this case the overall treatment model incorporates a wide range of evidence-based techniques within it.

The specifics of the new model begin to be outlined in Chapter 4 with the overall goals. In Chapter 5 the goals are operationalized into steps of the model. These chapters explain the roadmap and direction of treatment, while the vehicle to get there is based upon the training, experience and personal therapeutic approach of the therapist.

Chapter 6 moves into an even more practical section of the book designed to show how interventions flow from the goals and steps of the model. A step-by-step process is offered in this chapter describing the thought process involved in coming up with identifying the right problem, and then a process to determine solutions or interventions.

With the thought that it could be helpful to begin with a child with challenging issues and walk through the treatment process, the next three Chapters, 7, 8 and 9, provide real case examples. Each is different and each plan emphasizes a specific aspect of treatment the child needs.

The last chapter presents both the history and the approaches utilized by the treatment community where Neurological Reparative Therapy was developed. While the NRT model can be integrated into the practice of treatment professionals, it can also be implemented into a mental health service or organization. Chapter 10 outlines how this has developed over time at Jasper Mountain in Oregon.

The final section of the book, the Epilogue, explains why Neurological Reparative Therapy can be a useful model at present but it is not the full answer to helping clients, particularly children with challenging issues. The book starts with saying what the NRT model is not and the final chapter ends the discussion with the limitations of the model. There is a level of humility necessary when developing a new approach to impacting the most complex aspect of human beings — the brain. While it is hoped that the reader finds some value in these pages, this book and this treatment model does not pretend to have all the answers or constitute the best approach. The reader will only find the answers for specific questions as they take the journey of helping another human being. To the degree that Neurological Reparative Therapy can provide a map for the journey, it has accomplished its mission.

Chapter

1

The Need for a New Treatment Model

I am aware of some irony in writing this book presenting a new model of treatment. I say this because I have over the last four decades watched the many treatment models in psychology come and, for the most part, go out of use. Watching this pattern I observed just how long the latest new treatment du jour would remain popular and I told myself I would make it a point to avoid jumping onto bandwagons. So here I am joining the parade of treatment models, but with one important distinction that I will explain.

Before explaining the model, a question must be addressed regarding the need for a new treatment model given the many treatment approaches that are available. The answer is that psychology is in an excellent position to take advantage of the amazing new information that has and will continue to come from the study of the brain. Never in the history of mankind has there been an awakening quite like the one we are in right now. Compared to our current era of the brain, the Renaissance putting an end to the Dark Ages may come the closest by comparison. For the very first time, we have more than beliefs and theories about how we understand life and understand ourselves, we now have evidence. When Descartes said, "Cogito Ergo Sum" (I think therefore I am) he postulated that the mind is the foundational core of the self and the subjective experience of existence. We now know how we think, what we think, and why we think and this is only the beginning, we will learn much more about ourselves in the years ahead.

With every new advancement in our understanding, all new approaches that take advantage of new insight are not far behind. So it is with brain research and the explosion of new science surrounding the most complex organic structure in the known universe. The human brain is not only complex, it is what makes each of us what and who we are. It is what you are relying on when you read these words and what you must use to understand their meaning. It is what will determine the value or lack of that you find as you read further. In fact, the "you" in the last sentence is the part of the brain that has no physical substance and yet is the core of the subjective self – the mind.

As a result of the last two decades of an evolving understanding of the human brain, we know so much more than Descartes and, for that matter, so much more than Freud about what makes us who we are and what determines how we perceive, feel and behave. Given this new information, can new light be shed on working with the brain to maximize its potential, including the ability to understand itself? The answer is definitely yes and when it comes to evidence, what we used to believe or conjecture we can now actually know. If this sounds like a great time to integrate all this information into a new treatment model, then we would be in agreement.

It is hard to imagine any of the great theoreticians of psychology and human behavior not taking advantage of everything they could know about the human brain. I would also say that most would have altered their models to accommodate such new information. It is in this spirit that the new treatment model Neurological Reparative Therapy has developed and this has taken place in the crucible of clinical practice at Jasper Mountain, a special treatment program in Oregon. A brief way of explaining this new model is to examine the meaning of the three words in the title.

Neurological—Neurology is the study of the activity of the brain. Contrary to common belief neurons do not compose the majority of the cells in the brain, these would be the glial or support cells. But neurons are the most important cells in the brain and do the brain's heavy lifting. Every support cell in the brain is designed to serve and sustain the ability of the neurons to do the mental work it is capable of. Neurons are some of the most important and fascinating cells in the human body. They are the most vulnerable of all cells and yet they live longer than any other cells. A single neuron can last only a few minutes without ample oxygen and nourishment (glucose) and yet it can live and function for over 100 years when these basic needs are continually provided. The neuron is the basic unit of the brain and, being social in nature, neurons form larger and larger units and structures that allow the brain to do the many operations within its capacity. Although we do not as yet know the full potential of the brain or even every operation it can perform, we know enough to appreciate this most wondrous component of the human body.

To impact the perceptions, emotions and behavior of a person, we must impact the brain's neurons and neuronal clusters or networks. When the first word of the title of this new model is neurological, this correctly implies that NRT will seek to enlist the full potential of the neuronal systems of the brain to bring about improved or even optimum functioning. This model will also attempt to heighten the internal ability of the brain to literally change reality in the direction the individual chooses. In this way perceptual changes are changes in the person's reality. When this takes place on the inside of the brain, the outside of the brain then becomes subject to the individual's control and not the reverse. This neurological model of treatment can enable individuals to self-define and even experience a world they choose. With such power comes responsibility and at some point in the NRT process the individual must take responsibility for the world they are choosing to live in.

Reparative — The word repair implies that something is broken and needs to be made whole once again. It also implies that when it is repaired it once again achieves its natural state of completeness. Both statements are accurate in the case of damage done to and within the brain by external forces that have reduced the brain's capacity for self-determination and facilitating a state of optimal physical and mental health. The brain's natural state is a coordinated symphony of complex functions and abilities that (there is no better way to say it) boggle the mind.

The only thing capable of understanding the human brain is a human brain. The brain may be the best evidence one will ever find for what some call intelligent design. It is difficult to imagine an organic substance evolving coincidentally to have the ability to do all the brain can do. Regardless of its origins, the natural state of the brain is optimum functioning. Every aspect of brain development carefully facilitates both surviving and thriving. The brain is the key protective factor within the human being for survival. But unlike other members of the animal kingdom, in humans survival is only a part of what the brain has an instinctual drive to pursue. The brain has the ability to take a step back and consider its own conclusions and informed directions. The ability to self-reflect and self-correct are key to the brain's ability to get the most out of existence. Survival is critical, but thriving is what the brain secondarily can do when its own abilities are utilized.

4

Many events in life can impair the brain's ability to reach its optimal performance—trauma, stress, injury, disease and much more. Getting the brain back to what it does best often takes repairing the damage that has become the hindrance. Therefore, the second word in the title is the need and importance of repairing and making the natural state of the brain whole once again—promoting full use of complex systems and developing optimal mental health.

Therapy—This is a word indicating an active process. The term means to remediate, to rehabilitate and to return to full or optimum functioning. Therapy is a process of changing, realigning and restoring a state of wholeness. When added to the first two words, this new treatment model is an active process of restoring the optimal health of the human brain. The word therapy also implies a process that has a direction and component parts that when put together can promote success or reaching the desired destination. The destination of Neurological Reparative Therapy is the optimal functioning of the human brain resulting in a self-directed path in life, along with the awareness to plot the course and utilize the available internal gyroscope to stay on the path. To achieve this destination requires the active process of focused effort at the right time and in the right way.

All therapy requires oversight to determine if the desired results are being achieved. The beauty of NRT is that once the brain has been optimized, the oversight and self-righting mechanism are both internal. In this way the model promotes change from the inside out, and the more this process is repeated the more effective and successful it becomes. What begins as an externally driven process to repair the brain soon becomes an internal drive to keep the brain in good and potentially optimal condition.

Going beyond what the title implies about this new treatment model, Neurological Reparative Therapy can be said to be more of a roadmap than a technique. We are only recently learning what experiences damage the brain and how to repair this damage. For hundreds of years those interested in learning about the brain had to rely on observing the brain's structure in autopsies or anecdotal information. The famous example of Phineas Gage is a case in point. The following account of poor Phineas is of as much importance in what it reflects about how the brain was studied as in what was learned from one man's misfortune.

The Amazing Case of Phineas Gage and a Positive Update

Phineas Gage holds a special place in the modern era of brain research. He lived from 1823 to 1860 and as a 25 year-old adult working on the railroad he was injured when preparing to blast a hole in the rock on the rail line in Vermont. An accidental explosion occurred when he was tamping the blasting powder into a drilled hole with a 43" iron bar that weighed 13 pounds. The powder exploded and sent the iron tamping bar flying into the air and landing some 80 feet away. In the process of being airborne the bar passed through Gage's head, through the left cheek, traveling through the left frontal lobe and exiting the top of the skull. While certainly not the first person to have physical damage to the skull and brain, the amazing outcome that he survived the accident makes this one of the earliest and most studied cases of its type.

The Phineas Gage case is unique in several aspects. First, Gage survived the accident that caused profound damage to his brain. Second, the injury was localized and added to the understanding of how parts of the brain control brain functions. Third, Gage underwent a radical change in personality. Finally, only recently has the most important aspect of his case been recognized as an example of the brain's ability to adapt and recover functioning. This last point references the most recent information (within the last two years) that goes beyond the fact that Phineas Gage initially went from a hard working, stable, moral and socially appropriate young man before the injury to a less refined, irritable and somewhat crude individual after the accident. Therefore, the part of his brain that was damaged resulted in identifiable personality changes. Most psychology students who have heard of this case had information that stopped with the negative personality changes. However, there is new information that lends evidence to a very different outcome and very different message about damage to the brain. It appears that in the twelve years he lived following the accident, Gage was able to adapt and regain much of his earlier personality, contrary to the legend that surrounds this case (MacMillan, 2000; MacMillan, 2008). This new information turns this fascinating case of personality change into an even more important case of the brain's ability to heal and recover.

My point in briefly discussing the case of Phineas Gage is to highlight how difficult it has been in the past to learn about the brain. Even in this celebrated case, what was actually learned appears to have been repeatedly distorted over the years. The current study of the brain does not rely on anecdotes or autopsies but on real time evidence enabled by technologies such as Functional Magnetic Resonance Imaging and Positron Emission Tomography among other sophisticated brain scans. We can now study the brain in real time and this ability has been the primary reason for the explosion (with apologies to Phineas) of new insight into the workings of the brain. In the early to mid 1900s the followers of Watson and Skinner said that all therapy is behavioral therapy because this is all we can really impact. There are still some who might say this. In the early 2000s we have enough information to say that all therapy is neurological, and this includes but is not limited to our behavior. Neurological Reparative Therapy is an orientation to the understanding that we can and must impact the internal workings of the individual, the mind, as well as impact the externalization of the individual which includes perceptions, emotional expression and behaviors.

Jonah Was the Worst Kid He Had Ever Met

Before coming to Jasper Mountain, like his namesake in the Bible, Jonah had been swallowed up not by a whale but by his terrible past abuse and neglect. No one had to tell him his behavior was horrible and his attitude worse, he already knew this because he was by far the worst kid he had ever run into. His inner sense of himself was an expectation of being the biggest problem in any situation where he found himself. At Jasper he immediately tried to establish his role of the worst kid, the problem was he had considerable competition for the role. Before he realized it, he was losing the competition for finishing last, and liking something quite new – coming out on top. At first success bewildered him and he didn't know what to make of it. But over time he began to put the same energy it took to be the worst kid into doing well and he started having one success after another. His brain liked the results and his tantrums and rages turned into a quick complaint and he would move on. Success at school, success with peers, success in sports all completely changed his self-view. Through trauma treatment, daily skill training, and experiencing success, Jonah emerged from being swallowed by the past to a new day and a new future of having dreams and goals. The same child who was sure he would be the worst kid in any room now was sure of something else – he could reach his dreams!

There is no club to join, no expensive training or certification to enroll in. Neurological Reparative Therapy doesn't even ask that you change your treatment approach or your techniques. What's not to like? Add to this that this orientation to helping people realize the life they have always wanted and never knew was available promises to provide a roadmap to optimal brain health. This promise includes a map with milestones along the way including important destinations such as improving relationships and attachment, resolving old stress and handling current stress better, moving on from traumatic experiences, and maximizing the individual's executive functions and thus promoting self-regulation and self-determination.

Following every opportunity to understand aspects of the brain, as in the example of Phineas Gage, how science viewed the brain and how science sought to impact and heal the brain had to be altered. With the advent of new forms of technology, our understanding and appreciation are changing daily. It is time to integrate this new understanding into psychology and the helping professions. For this to be accomplished a new treatment model is needed.

While promising to clarify the road to optimal mental and emotional health, Neurological Reparative Therapy cannot promise success for either the client or the therapist. Maps are not the journey, the journey is the active process of movement, discovery and risk and only the traveler can do this. However, a poor map can hinder the process and may even put in doubt arrival at the intended destination. A map also cannot promise that the traveler will stay committed, stay vigilant and not lose interest and focus. Once again only the traveler can do this. On the other hand, no form of treatment can promise these things and those that do should be avoided.

Therefore, is it accurate to call Neurological Reparative Therapy a new model? The answer is yes, but it does not claim to be the only model to arrive at the desired destination, nor can it self-righteously be called 'the one true treatment model.' Any approach with such a claim should also be avoided. NRT is one framework of implementing new information. The NRT model is battle tested and has been successful when little else showed any promise, and it has emerged from the foundation of the latest science on the human brain.

If you are interested in learning more, then the chapters ahead will provide a detailed explanation in both professional and practical language and examples. But before we go any further there is one more promise to make if you read this book—even if you take with you limited elements of this new model, you will emerge a better therapist, better helper, and have a better understanding of your own brain and how it understands and connects with other brains. You might consider viewing this as a no-lose investment of your time.

A New Treatment Model

For lasting change focus on the brain.

Problem behaviors arise from mental perception causing feelings resulting in reactive behaviors.

Neurological—the brain is the source of perceptions, change the brain and change the person.

Reparative—return the brain to the natural state of positive health and well-being.

Therapy—an active process of promoting change and facilitating healthy functioning.

For better or worse the brain is the source of the personality.

Neurological Reparative Therapy is a roadmap; the therapist must be the vehicle for the process.

Chapter

2

Neurological Reparative Therapy — What It Is and What It Is Not

This chapter is designed to state in clear terms what this new model is all about as well as what it does not purport to be. Neurological Reparative Therapy is a treatment model that integrates the most recent brain research to inform the direction of psychological treatment. Stress, trauma and the psychological damage that comes from the many negative experiences in life produce some consistent impacts on the individual's ability to cope and bounce back from adversity. As a result of recent research, a clear understanding about how traumatic events negatively affect the brain and nervous system of individuals is coming into focus. As this picture of negative impacts developed, simultaneous clarity is developing regarding how the brain can heal and learn to cope with even the most traumatic events. We must now learn to incorporate the inner healing ability of the body and the brain to respond to debilitating events.

The influx of new information about the brain and how it works is directly attributable to technology. Understanding the functions of the brain has been a specific interest for as long as it has been known that the brain is a major control center of the body. This has occurred over the last 300 years. Like astronomy and microbiology, the medical science of studying the human brain did not lend itself to direct observation until there were tools to do just that. With the invention of the telescope came a new appreciation of the vastness of the heavens around us. Hans Lippershey, not Galileo, was the first of many inventors to formally register the telescope with a patent around 1608. Although only magnifying an image by the power of 3, the new technology became the start of understanding the sky by observation rather than theory or superstition. In a similar way, Anton van Levenhuk is credited with the discovery of the microscope in the late 1700s. Soon after came a new interest in and series of discoveries related to the tiny worlds we have around us and microbiology was the outgrowth.

It is important to point out that long before there was technology to lend some science to the vast heavens above or microscopic worlds on the head of a pin, there had long been human interest leading to postulations and beliefs. Beliefs that could not be studied or proven were often linked to religious doctrine, as Galileo and many other aspiring scientists found out. Beliefs were the realm of the unknown and were not subject to evidence. Beliefs belong in the world of religion and faith rather than science. We do not say that we believe there is a place named Seattle because we know there is such a place from our own experience or the experience of others. Religion has beliefs, but science has theories and these two are not the same. The best distinction is that theories can be proven or disproven but the same cannot be said of beliefs. Religion and science have never had a more harmonious coexistence than in modern times because both are different paradigms and one cannot take the place of the other as in Galileo's time. The advent of specific technologies has moved the brain into the world of science since it can now be observed, measured and directly studied.

The human brain is much the same as astronomy and microbiology in that substantial progress had to wait until neurobiology had the tools to allow scientific observation. Prior to the very recent

14

breakthroughs in technology, equivalent to the telescope and microscope, scientists had to resign themselves to post-hoc direct examination of yet another universe that was the frontier of the human brain and the seat of the self. Theories and beliefs abounded as to the workings of the brain. In fact the intense scientific study of the brain dates back to the era of the telescope and microscope with Thomas Willis in 1665 first using the term "neurology"(Hughes, 1991) and Franz Joseph Gall in 1775 first postulating that the brain has separate regions that had separate functions, a radical theory for the time (Young, 1990).

The equivalent of the telescope and the microscope that facilitated the scientific understanding of the brain are machines that observe deep within the brain without causing any harm to the individual. First, the X-Ray provided an ability to see within the skull of a living person, but only with limitations. The Computed Tomography, commonly known as the CAT Scan, would open up new possibilities along with offshoots such as the Positron Emissions Tomography (PET Scan), and Magnetic Resonance Imaging (MRI) or Functional Magnetic Resonance Imaging (FMRI). Each of these tools allowed the scientist to do what the telescope and microscope had previously done, allowed direct scientific observation of a dynamic environment.

With the invention of new tools and the benefit of direct scientific observation to confirm or disprove theories, the next step in the scientific process is to implement the new information into models to understand and help the human race. At the risk of sounding melodramatic, Neurological Reparative Therapy is one such model. It is a practical application of the new understandings of the brain to advance the prevention and treatment of neurological disorders. The term neurological disorders is used in a broad sense and includes how the brain is involved in distress of all types. Specific neurological disorders of particular interest include traumatic experiences, poor neuro-integration, and impaired social attachment. Each of these are common disorders in mental health settings.

Neurological Reparative Therapy Assists in Trauma Treatment

NRT is a treatment model that can assist with the treatment of trauma. After traumatic experiences the perceptual system of the human brain can change radically. The brain may become hypersensitive to any threats to survival, as well it should. The world has been an unsafe place since the dawn of mankind and this theme continues today. Whether you prefer intelligent design or natural selection, the human brain is prepared to assist survival in any way that it can. The brain experiences traumatic events as serious threats to survival and adapts immediately to the threat. While it is a positive adaptation for someone to avoid the rattling snake in the future following an unfortunate and painful past experience, it is often a negative adaptation to avoid all opportunities of intimacy following an unpleasant sexual experience as a teen.

The primal region of the brain that remembers, assesses, and produces protective counter measures (flight or fight) has little time to send a memo to the prefrontal cortex for detailed analysis. Therefore the limbic region of the brain does not discriminate between perceived threats since false positives (a perceived threat that turns out to be benign) are preferable to death.

There are practical problems with the way the brain processes threats, not the least of which is how an immediate response to a perceived threat takes precedence over thoughtful consideration, seeing the big picture, and every other executive function and higher order mental process. The reactive limbic region of the brain in a way does its job much too well, particularly following a traumatic experience. When we are on a road trip and hungry we notice the restaurant signs along the way. When we buy a new car we notice everyone's vehicle more intensely and when we put our house up for sale we notice all the 'For Sale' signs. This phenomenon is called salient perception. What we perceive around us is stimulated by an experience that makes a particular aspect of the environment more important or salient. Traumatic experiences make threats and associations related to negative experiences salient to the degree that the higher order reasoning centers of the brain often shut down allowing immediate and total reactivity to avoid the perceived threat.

In our modern world, as in every other era of human experience, threats are all around us. All modes of transportation carry the risk of injury or death, nearly all social contact carries the risk of at least emotional pain. Even in our homes we face environmental threats from within and a host of threats from without. Following a traumatic experience, the triggers to the threat may be generalized causing the brain to be on high alert much of the time. The younger the child who experiences a traumatic event, the more likely the high alert state is to cause chronic toxic stress.

The goals and steps of NRT are highly compatible with the effective treatment of trauma, improved self-regulation and the ability to handle stress. Both change the perceptual system of the brain by enhancing the ability of the prefrontal cortex to apply higher order reasoning to experiences around the individual. Both attempt to put the individual back in charge of the overactive stress response cycle—stress, hormonal activation, fight or flight response, repeat cycle. Effective trauma therapy will have very similar goals as NRT making the two modes of treatment not only compatible but indistinguishable in many respects.

Neurological Reparative Therapy Facilitates Neuro-Integration

Throughout this book the term neuro-integration will be used to describe the essential ability of the brain to coordinate the mental processes going on in all brain regions. The importance of this coordination, sometimes referred to as neural integration, will become abundantly clear.

The brain remains an organic structure that is sophisticated beyond our current understanding. Such a highly evolved structure requires internal communication and overall coordination or the result is chaos. Visualize the New York Philharmonic with over 100 highly trained virtuosos in their own right all in the same room playing at the same time. Without the score or conductor, the result would be less impressive than it would be irritating and even painful. However, add the essential ingredients of first an overarching focus, but even then all instruments are not playing the same notes in the same way. Now add the cohesion of the maestro and the result can truly be an experience in synergy, where the music produced is more than the sum of its individual components.

The brain can be such a fine-tuned orchestra multiplied billions of times because while there are a somewhat manageable number of regions with diverse and developed functions, these regions are composed of 100 billion individual components, some more practiced than others.

Using another analogy, the pre-frontal cortex of the brain is a sophisticated Federal Aviation Administration (FAA) control tower. It has highly sensitive and specialized technology for communication, awareness, and directional systems. However the control tower needs one more critical element to have the desired result which is a safe and smooth running overall aviation system. To accomplish the main goal the control tower must have air traffic controllers, the primary ingredient that puts the sophisticated technology to its intended use. The pre-frontal cortex is the terminus of the wiring of the human body, much like the control tower. The air traffic controller of the brain is the orbitofrontal cortex. The essential elements of mental coordination and the resulting mental health are all of the mental orchestral components that are well practiced and focused along with communication, awareness and directional intentionality. The critically important final link is the decision maker or maestro of the brain, the orbitofrontal cortex. The use of the orchestra and FAA control tower are other ways of describing neuro-integration.

Many problems can arise that impair or prevent neuro-integration. Component regions of the brain may be undeveloped, for example, with a learning disability. Communication involving sensory input as well as between brain regions may be impaired, for example, with an injury or neurological disorder such as Multiple Sclerosis. Perhaps the most common deficiency of neuro-integration is the lack of overall coordination or an undeveloped pre-frontal cortex. For example, the individual who experiences significant trauma may have an orbitofrontal cortex that has not developed to the degree it needs to. In the years ahead, a number of mental health issues will likely be considered under a new category called a deficiency of neuro-integration.

Neurological Reparative Therapy helps repair as well as promote the development of neuro-integration. This treatment model can enhance component parts of the brain to work together through enhanced communication, brain region development, and overall coordination through the development of the all important decision-making aspect of the brain. NRT helps improve optimal mental health which can be defined as a brain that has very developed regions with maximized complex functions, with the learned ability to be mentally flexible, and all the complex brain regions working in harmony.

Neurological Reparative Therapy Enhances Attachment

Human beings are social animals and are not meant to be isolated from others if the goal is a full and positive life experience. However, just being around each other does not necessarily produce community or the supportive interaction of people enhancing growth and positive development in others. Sometimes more than one person in a room produces conflict. The necessary ingredient for positive social experience revolves around the concept of attachment. This is not to say that we go through life repeatedly trying to bond and attach to everyone we meet, this would be an unworkable and chaotic experience in frustration and failure. This means that the components of social success that will be needed throughout life are learned in the experience of attachment early in life.

Humans do not do well when isolated from others, but they also don't do well if they do not know how to positively interact with others around them. This is the dilemma of many individuals with inadequate social skills. Happiness in life is heavily connected to social involvement, social support and social success. The same is true for good mental health which requires us to positively manage and cope with the stress of living as well as the stress of dying. Coping with stress is first learned through the bond with a caring and nurturing parent. For those individuals who received inadequate early nurturing or even received the opposite, living with the stress of life can be overwhelming. Without assistance to learn how to attach to others when this early experience was disrupted or unavailable early in life, the individual may well develop one of many mental health disorders.

The dilemma of the individual who experienced early impaired attachment in life is that they need people, but avoid people due to mistrust and unwillingness to be vulnerable. This dilemma must be addressed if the individual is to have a chance at a fulfilling life and some measure of personal contentment along the way.

Neurological Reparative Therapy can assist in the development or repair of attachment. It can help by addressing the specific barriers to bonding to others in a positive way. Impediments to attachment include the mistrust and misperception of the motives of others that are common results of traumatic experiences. The lack of an early and successful bonding experience with a parent can produce a cascading series of challenges to good mental health. Unsuccessful attachment increases stress levels and often prevents the learned ability to cope with stress. Early bonding problems often result in problems of self-regulation making many, if not most, challenges in life even more difficult than they need to be. Early attachment problems impair the internally driven ability to focus and creates hyper-arousal to threats, both real and imagined. The problems cascade due to the reluctance of the person to be vulnerable to others and therefore experience deficits in learning pro-social skills. In other words, the less practice the person has at improving social skills, the more deficient the person becomes over time.

NRT can bring a focus of treatment to the barriers of attachment. It all starts with helping individuals see how their brain is processing the world and the people around them. This treatment model promotes the development of skills necessary to successfully bond with others. It includes attention to traumatic memory and any negative adaptations that have resulted. Perhaps the most important way that NRT assists in rehabilitating attachment is to have the therapist become an appropriate and positive attachment figure during the process so that the client experiences the positive rewards of successfully connecting with another human being.

Neurological Reparative Therapy Promotes Resiliency

Life is not only filled with stress, it also has abundant negative and even traumatic events. Bad things happen in everyone's life. The older one gets, the frequency of bad things often increases such as health challenges, negative aspects of aging, and the increased presence of death the longer the individual lives. Another reality is that whatever we attempt to learn, we usually have to fail repeated times before we experience smaller and then greater success. In order to become proficient at most things, we must learn how to handle repeated failure. This ability is called resiliency or the ability to bounce back when either something bad happens or we fail at something. Because life has so many challenges, resiliency is an essential component to developing optimal mental health and finding personal contentment.

Nowhere is resiliency more important than in social connections with others. Individuals must learn the process of "Rupture and Repair" (Siegel, 2010). Not only do we struggle in intimate and all important relationships and connections with others, but relationships are forged and improved through difficulty. While humans have an instinctive drive to connect with others, we also have a human tendency to run for cover when we run into intimate conflicts. Our brain wants to protect us and sometimes it does not do well in distinguishing between a physical threat, a threat to our feelings or even our fragile ego. Rejection is the greatest threat in relationships and some of the most difficult times in our lives have been times of significant rejections — the end of a friendship, not getting into the desired school, cut from the team, being fired from a job, or perhaps a divorce. These can be very painful times, at least right at the time. At these times we need to understand how we perceive the situation, what has and has not happened, and how to repair the damage. Resiliency requires both a clear perceptual understanding of the situation at hand as well as the ability to cope with the inherent challenges. The perceptual understanding requires an ability to self-reflect, a distinctively human attribute enabled by the brain. Human emotions can be powerful, particularly the negative emotions of frustration, anger, fear and hopelessness. Such strong emotions cloud or prevent insight and looking at the larger picture. The young man who is rejected by a love interest may feel at that moment that life has lost all meaning and love will never again be available. To put a rejection or negative experience into context requires an awareness of the strong emotions and the ability to perceive a larger picture. "She rejected me and it is painful but I am seventeen and perhaps I will live to love another day." Actually, for most seventeen year olds in such a situation this insight must come from the outside. As the individual matures it is important for such insight to be internalized, "I lost this job that I loved, but I am skilled and I can find something perhaps even better." This is resilient thinking, the ability to put negative experiences into a broader context.

Another essential element of resiliency is coping. We don't have to win all the battles we are presented with in life, but it helps if we can cope with as many difficulties as possible. Coping only comes from experience. This is why individuals who have successfully faced very difficult experiences in life handle stress better than those who have not been so forcefully challenged. The ability to cope comes from the experience of positive responses to stress. Often times when an individual faces stress, the stress wins the day. Coping is the experience of facing stress and coming out on top or being able to manage the difficulty. The more challenging the situation, the possibility exists for a more productive outcome on the individual's self-perception based on positive coping.

Beth Just Knew She Would Never Succeed

Beth entered our program from an early abusive environment with a belief that her life would never get better. The world she knew was neglect, sexual abuse and witnessing sadistic violence to people and animals. In foster homes Beth hurt people and animals herself, repeating a pattern that was familiar to her. She wanted to care about others but it was too stressful and frightening. Her brain had been trained to quickly react as though her life was in danger. In our program, her internal stress decreased with a very predictable environment. Her executive functions were improved to process her experiences, decreasing her panic and giving her alternatives to tantrums and violence. In trauma treatment, she gradually learned to cope with the past. Over time her treatment gave her a greater sense of control and power and a full range of emotional expression. Her behavior improved because she gave consideration to her actions. Beth has hard times ahead, and her problems are not over, but she has begun to realize that her life is getting better after all.

Renee Villanueva, M.Ed.

24

The physiological explanation of coping is the ability to manage the stress response cycle of the hypothalamus sensing stress and signaling the release of corticotropin release factor that stimulates the brain's pituitary and adrenal glands to secrete adrenaline, norepinephrine, and cortisol. This activation process produces the fight or flight response to the perceived threat or stress. Coping occurs when the individual is able to have some influence on the intensity of the activation process and thus reserving a full fight or flight response to only those situations when truly needed. A driver may be faced on a daily basis with the inherent and real stress of being on the busy freeway with other drivers, some who may be impaired or angry or simultaneously talking on a cell phone while putting on makeup and eating an egg muffin. The ability of the driver to overcome such stress day after day builds the confidence of the individual to manage the stress and thus they have learned over time to cope with freeway driving. Take a driver from a small rural area and place them on the same city freeway and the stress of the experience may be perceived as life threatening and traumatic.

In a very real sense, resiliency is the healing mechanism of the brain. It is also the basis for an aspect of the philosophy of Fredrick Nietzsche which is symbolized in the often quoted but not universally true statement, "What does not kill me, makes me stronger" (Nietzsche, 1888). Like the muscle cells of the body, neurons in the brain grow stronger with stimulation. It is also true that neuronetworks grow in complexity, communication and capacity with use. In these functional ways, repetition and experiences produce growth and development of capacities of coping. When bad things happen to an individual, the ability to bounce back, resiliency, is the quickest way to healing and moving on.

Of course NRT does not do any of the things mentioned above, the therapist and the client do them. What NRT does is to provide a roadmap to focus on each of these important components of optimal health—healing from trauma, enhancing neuro-integration, improving attachment and promoting resiliency.

What Neurological Reparative Therapy Is Not

At the beginning of Chapter 1 it is stated that there is a difference between Neurological Reparative Therapy and other treatment models. The difference is NRT is not a treatment approach so much as a direction for treatment to pursue. There are a multitude of treatment techniques or what I consider the therapeutic vehicle to go from where the client is to the desired destination. NRT is not a vehicle; it is more like a roadmap. This distinction is important as a fundamental principle of the NRT orientation. This new model does not presume to tell the practitioner how to facilitate the therapeutic process. While there has been a strong focus on research-based treatment approaches and techniques over the last two decades, evidence-based practice cannot supplant the expertise and experience of the individual practitioner. This point is too often overlooked in the discussions of evidence-based practices in therapy. While a research base enhances the credibility of an approach or technique, the best evidence-based approach will fail in the hands of an unskilled or incompetent practitioner. Some of the strongest evidence of successful treatment comes from adherence to recognized treatment components facilitated by a skilled practitioner (Lambert & Bergen, 1994).

Neurological Reparative Therapy respects the individuality and expertise of the practitioner and encourages the therapist to use his or her own skills and experience in combination with research-based techniques as the vehicle to facilitate the treatment process.

Despite the primary emphasis on evidence-based practices, there is substantial research support over many decides that the treatment technique employed is only a small contributor to the success or lack of success in the therapeutic process (Asay & Lambert, 1999; Bergin & Garfield, 1994). Following sixty years of research, the strongest evidence comes down to the impact of a competent therapist who skillfully facilitates a process of understanding, catharsis, insight and exploration within a therapeutic alliance. What NRT provides is a roadmap to the understanding, insight and exploration that leads to the type of repair needed to return the brain to more optimal functioning. Once again the distinction between destination and approach is important because the best destination will prove allusive without a vehicle to get there, and the best vehicle is of little use unless it proceeds in the right direction toward a desired destination.

In the chapters ahead, Neurological Reparative Therapy will provide a map for the process of repairing the brain and why a focus on the brain is the critical element to operationalize brain research and facilitating movement toward mental, emotional and behavioral health. Therefore NRT is not the full answer by any means. When taking a trip, consulting a map is one of many important ingredients to a successful journey. While not the only component of increasing the odds of a successful therapeutic process, using this approach and following the intervention protocol could make a major difference in the outcome and will be illustrated in a number of case examples throughout the book.

NRT—What It Is and Is Not

The brain is the new frontier of science.

Trauma therapy is enhanced by NRT.

A fundamental aspect of NRT is brain coordination or neuro-integration.

Attachment is explained and aided by NRT.

Resiliency is an important component of NRT.

NRT is not a technique or specific practice, it is an overarching model that integrates brain science into any method of treatment.

NRT is a model that can make a good therapist even better.

Chapter

3

The Foundation of Neurological Reparative Therapy

Neurological Reparative Therapy developed as a model for treatment based upon the research and literature from the specialty areas of brain science, trauma studies, resiliency and attachment research. The first question some ask, "Is NRT an evidenced-based practice?' The answer to this question is that NRT is a model for treatment and not a practice. As such it is based upon a solid foundation of research and the professional literature of a number of related disciplines. The four specialty areas of brain science, trauma, resiliency and attachment are not often considered together, but when they are they weave together to form a fabric of healing and human potential. In this chapter some of the literature from each of these areas will be briefly addressed as the science that forms the foundation of NRT.

Brain Development Literature

Advancements in understanding the brain have been the primary reason for the development of Neurological Reparative Therapy. In a real sense this entire book is about the understanding and implementation of brain science to promote positive functioning. A significant amount of literature is available to help understand how the brain functions (Hariri, 2006; Kagan, 2010; Perry, 1994; Restak, 2001). Additional research has been conducted on the neurobiological process of attachment (Schore, 2001; Siegel, 2010).

The impact of traumatic experiences on the brain has abundant literature (van der Kolk, Perry & Herman, 1991; Ziegler, 2002). The final thread in this fabric of understanding and using the brain to promote mental health is the research and literature on resiliency. The understanding of each of these components of functioning is based on knowing how the brain works. Therefore brain science can be viewed as the umbrella under which each of these specialty areas is found. Attention will now be directed at each of these areas individually.

Trauma Literature

Few subjects in psychology have received the amount of attention given to trauma and its effects on the brain, emotions and behavior. It has long been recognized that individuals frequently make radical changes in functioning due to negative experiences such as loss, grief, injury and other aspects of life that challenge people's ability to cope. It has only been in recent history, approximately the last 100 years, where psychology as a science began a systematic study of the adverse impacts of negative experiences. The term trauma is generally considered to be any experience that overrides the internal ability of the individual to cope with the situation. Therefore, inherent in the very definition of trauma is the response of the person more than the event itself. What may be traumatic for one person may not be for someone else; trauma is highly individualized.

The adverse effects of trauma can have negative ramifications for an individual's internal sense of self as well as impacting the ability to positively engage with others. Starting with internal changes, perhaps the primary impact of trauma is getting stuck and organizing one's life around the negative experience and avoiding any repetition. In serious cases such negative focus and avoidance can develop into posttraumatic stress disorder, a potentially debilitating condition.

Serious negative experiences affect the way the brain processes information by sending all sensory information through a filter in the limbic system that is hypervigilant to any hint of the past trauma. This limbic reactivity can profoundly alter the way the brain works in areas such as understanding external events, accessing higher order reasoning centers, coping with emotional experiences, and being able to focus on academic learning. All these areas significantly change the individual from within.

With an affected ability to understand emotions, the individual often has an impaired ability to use feelings as a guide to decision-making. Without an accurate understanding of external events and the motivations of others, the prefrontal cortex struggles to take advantage of helpful input from the limbic region of the brain because the limbic signals are sounding an alarm concerning sensory input related to stored trauma memory in the hippocampus. Another common outgrowth of the heightened state of awareness is affective blindness or not understanding or responding to the feelings of others. This unresponsiveness produces distance and impaired bonding with others and negatively affects a support system.

Another internal impact of traumatic experience is a resulting decrease of blood flow to specific regions of the brain such as areas of speech. This can impact the ability of the individual, particularly a child, to communicate verbally his or her internal experience. Additional internal impacts include a personal sense of feeling powerless over the events in the person's life resulting in a pervasive negativity, impaired personal confidence, and not being able to trust others resulting in personal isolation.

A common outgrowth of traumatic experience crosses the line between internal and external harm. Trauma frequently causes a loss of self-regulation, which is both an internal dynamic when the individual is overwhelmed with the pressures of living and an external dynamic with expressions of negative emotions and unmodulated behavior. Self-regulation must be a major focus of treatment for those who struggle in this area. In a similar crossover between internal and external impact, the traumatized individual may align their awareness with stimuli related to the stress. In doing so he or she may underreact to non-threat (unimportant) stimuli and overreact to perceived threat (critically important) stimuli (van der Kolk, et. al., 1991).

Adding to the list of negative external manifestations of trauma experiences, violent behavior may be increased. Trauma can activate the brainstem functions such as respiration, heart rate and blood pressure, which simultaneously decrease higher order limbic and cortical functions. With an increased reactive system on alert and a decreased ability to bring reason and consideration to the event, the result could be a violent response.

A great deal more has been written about each of the above impacts of trauma. An excellent example is a pivotal book, *Traumatic Stress, the Effects of Overwhelming Experiences on the Mind, Body and Society* (van der Kolk, McFarlane & Weisaeth, 1996). In the years since it was published, more has been learned but it remains an excellent overview.

There are a large number of other adverse impacts of trauma but most of these could fit into one or more of the above dynamics. In general, traumatic experiences negatively change lives by impairing the internal ability of the brain to take in sensory information, process it critically and on its own merits, and develop functional responses that positively engage with others and the environment to gain support and meet the needs and wants of the individual. Neurological Reparative Therapy must impact all these adverse impacts to allow the individual to take advantage of the ability to cope, heal and to move beyond negative experiences.

Attachment Literature

While significant attention is given to trauma in the professional literature, the focus given to attachment is not far behind. Much of the credit for our understanding of the essential nature of attachment goes to John Bowlby, an English psychoanalyst who initially was interested in how children responded to grief and loss. His work in this area would result in attachment theory, still regarded today after 50 years as a cornerstone of conceptualizing the process of the bond between the child and the parent (Bowlby, 1982).

The significance placed on attachment by Bowlby, Ainsworth, Main and many researchers after them was not overstated. The quality of the attachment with the mother is the first step in life either toward success or failure in social functioning. There is little doubt that the attachment process begins before the child's birth and continues in the early years of childhood, adolescence and adulthood. The early times in the child's life sets in place a series of events that will either prepare the child to successfully face the challenges of living or create a reactive posture where the pressures of living will frequently be too much to manage. Because attachment affects coping, it overlaps with and must be considered when assessing traumatic experiences.

Attachment begins to influence the child first within the brain. The brain develops based upon several criteria that are heavily influenced by attachment. The brain matures from the more primitive to more complex functions. As the more complex regions of the brain develop, such as the limbic and neocortex, attachment will play a significant role. The brain will develop many more neurons early in life than it will need. This excess capacity appears to be related to enabling the brain to optimally adapt to a wide range of possibilities found in the environment. How the neurons come to develop networks or neural maps will be heavily influenced by attachment (Sroufe, Egeland, Carlson, & Collins, 2005; Greenberg, Speltz & DeKlyen, 1993). The process of use dependent development determines which neurons will form the networks of the brain and which will die and be pruned in the early years of life (Perry, Pollard, Blakely, Baker & Vigilante, 1995). The process of neurons connecting in networks is facilitated by how they communicate through chemical signals described in the frequently quoted statement, "when neurons fire together they wire together" (Voigt, Baier & De Lima, 1997).

As the brain develops it is significantly influenced by early experiences in both structure and operation (hardware and software), and no experiences will be more influential than the quality of the attachment the child develops. The physical structure of the brain will be influenced by experiences and by how it builds the capacity to perform the many critical functions the brain must perform. Therefore the brain develops around both experience and the functions it performs. A primary result of attachment experiences helps to develop what has been called the child's inner "working model" (Bowlby, 1982). This is the conceptual framework the child will use to appraise, interpret and regulate social and emotional information throughout life.

The child's inner working model will play an important role in forming the personality, determining emotional and social development and will even influence physical health and impact the individual's lifespan (Schore, 1994).

The neural networks that are developed from strong or weak attachments heavily influence the brain. Therefore all aspects of the individual are impacted since it is through strong attachments that neural networks of comfort, self-regulation and optimism are produced. Weak attachments can produce neural networks of reactivity, hypervigilance and pessimism. The quality of developing attachments heavily influences the developing personality of the individual. The process of a developing attachment has been called by many names such as contingent responsivity (Schore, 2001) and attunement of resonance centers of the brain between mother and child (Siegel, 2003). Either the child experiences the safety and support needed for surviving and thriving or the child does not, the brain will adapt to either contingency and the results will be one of the most profound influences on the child's life.

The neurobiological process of attachment is complex and fascinating and will only be briefly reviewed here. The very first experience of the child is literally being one with the attachment figure. For some time after birth, the child ideally has a continuation of the womb experience by experiencing the warmth, touch, and nurturing of the mother and a continuation of the experience of connectedness. The right hemisphere of the brain develops first and facilitates bonding behaviors with the mother (Trevarthen, 1998; Wittling & Pfluger, 1990). In a similar fashion, the right frontal cortex develops first forming the resonance center enabling attunement with the mother (Siegel, 2003). The brain is in a rapid period of development in the first two years of life and the quality of attachment will impact the brain's critical orientation to social adjustment, mood control, drive and responsibility, and defining the personality (Cavada & Schultz, 2000). As the brain matures, the emotional and sensory areas of the brain develop based upon the quality of attachment (Hariri & Holmes, 2006; Schore, 2001). The developing inner working model and a unified sense of self will be important to the development of empathy, morality and a moral guidance system throughout life.

The foundations of resiliency are preset during these early years of life. The attunement between the child and the mother, more precisely when the right frontal cortex of the child has resonance with the right frontal cortex of the mother, results in a mutually satisfying connection. For example, when an infant cries the attuned mother will comfort the child and provide soothing touch, speak in a soft voice and give comfort in any way she can. This creates a bond that provides security, comfort and the ability to handle stress, enabling self-regulation and the ability to cope with challenges — all major problem areas with children with poor early attachment (Spangler, Schieche, Ilg, Maier & Ackerman, 1994). Resiliency is first established with the help of the mother, and the mother/child attunement develops a "rupture and repair" process that forms the base of bouncing back from adversity (Schore, 2003).

Attachment cannot be discussed without giving consideration to human touch. Touch is the first language of a child and it is through touch that attachment is first communicated. Touch communicates safety, comfort and well-being, and it is often overlooked that human touch is a basic need. Research has connected touch with the activation of the orbitofrontal cortex and with the release of the neurotransmitter oxytocin. Research has linked oxytocin with trust, an essential ingredient of attachment.

This would help explain chronic low levels of oxytocin found in children raised in orphanages (Fries, Ziegler, Kurian, Jacoris & Pollak, 2005). Few would question the importance of touch in forming attachment with infants. However it is a very different matter with older children. The importance of touch is not only seldom acknowledged, touch is intentionally discouraged in the environments where children with attachment issues live and learn. Schools discourage staff touching children, coaches and mentors are discouraged from touching children and even foster homes and residential treatment programs are pressured by system regulators to avoid touching children in many situations, particularly when a child is having an emotional or behavioral meltdown. It is precisely when a child does not have the internal confidence to cope with a situation that reassurance of supportive touch becomes a basic need. The emotional regulation and soothing that should have been provided by touch and bonding at birth continues to be needed as children mature in our schools and systems of care.

To this point we have referred to the bond between mother and child. While the mother is most frequently the attachment figure and the natural process would rely on the mother/child bond, there are other possible attachment figures such as the father, adoptive or foster parents, grandparents, relatives, and others. When the mother is the primary figure of attachment, the father gradually becomes a more important part of the picture over the first two years (Schaffer & Emerson, 1964).

Attachment is such a pivotal process due in part to its impact on positive brain development, inner working model, developing personality, social orientation, emotional health, self-soothing and self-regulation, and resiliency. There is little in either the child or adult that has not been significantly influenced by the quality of early attachment. Poor early attachment can have a wide range of adverse results, including increased right subcortical activity which predisposes the individual to negative affect, then aggressive feelings, and finally violent behavior (Raine, Melroy & Bihrle, 1998; Perry, 2000) and intense and prolonged stress that can negatively impact emotional stability and the ability to trust others (Gaensbauer & Hiatt, 1984).

As would be expected from the important role of attachment, a poor attachment early in life has been associated with a wide range of problems including: poor self-regulation (van der Kolk, et. al., 1996), poor coping (Schore, 2001), undeveloped resiliency (DeBellis, Baum, Birmaher, Keshaven, Eccard, & Boring, 1999), abnormal social and moral development (Henshaw & Anderson, 1996), and an increased risk of psychopathology (Heim & Nemeroff, 1999) to name a few. The best antidote to a toxic and traumatic past is to promote positive attachment with all adults in a child's life including parents, extended family, teachers, therapists, coaches, mentors and direct care staff in treatment centers (Sprinson & Berrick, 2010).

Since attachment plays such a critical role in the development of the brain, the personality, and the prospects for success in life, attachment should be an important component in therapy, particularly for children. The following are a variety of ways that attachment can be improved in a therapeutic environment:

- Consistent experience of safety
- Predictable setting
- Excitement and relaxation are present and the allostatic process (the ability to become stimulated and return to a state of calm) is learned

- Presence of support from multiple sources
- Stimulating setting that promotes learning and accepts mistakes
- Childlike play is encouraged
- Expression is promoted in both genuine positive and negative forms
- Enjoyment instilled in life-long learning
- Instruction of all desired skill sets
- Social skills are learned primarily through social inclusion
- Modeling of empathy is provided
- Vulnerability and interpersonal risk-taking is modeled and encouraged
- Instilling moral reasoning and higher human aspirations
- Promoting the development of executive functions.

The single most significant impact therapy can have on an individual is to improve the ability of the person to form positive and lasting attachments with others. The rewards of strong attachments are great and the consequences of poor attachments are pervasive.

Resiliency and Positive Psychology Literature

An essential ability for a long and successful life is being able to bounce back from adversity, or what is referred to as resiliency. Over the last two decades a branch of psychology has been much more interested in what is right with people rather than what is wrong with them. This orientation is called positive psychology and it offers very useful information and approaches to help individuals bounce back from difficulties. Resiliency is built upon a number of skills and attitudes. The foundation of resiliency is built upon believing in yourself, having personal confidence, being able to connect in a positive way with others and allowing others to support you. Added to these important elements are having the experience that someone has confidence in you and it also has been shown in research that reaching out to help others improves resiliency (Pillemer, Fuller-Rowell, Reid, & Wells, 2010; Brown, Nesse, Vinokur, & Smith, 2003; Bernstein, 2003). For many children who have grown up in less than optimal environments, a healing, growth producing setting can build upon each of these elements of resiliency and enhance the child's world.

The most important attitudinal perspective to promoting resiliency is a positive outlook. There is substantial research that supports the healing qualities of a positive disposition (Miller, 2005; Lyubomirsky, King & Diener, 2005; Zautra, 2003). Without the ability to bounce back from adversity, a very negative lifelong trajectory is not only possible but likely including: loss of a real childhood, loss of self-regulation, isolation throughout life, poor relationships and poor social support, and negative affective states such as chronic fear, anger and depression. The combination of these factors may lead to mental health, criminal justice and/ or substance abuse problems and even a shorter life span due to physical disease brought on by chronic stress. The ability to turn this pattern in a positive direction is essential and resiliency is what it takes to do just that. In this way resiliency is linked with the previously discussed issues of attachment and trauma.

The negative trajectory of being overwhelmed by adversity in life can be countered by the positive cycle formed by a resilient response to life that promotes good physical health, reduced depression, greater happiness, and a longer life span (Seligman, 2002). However resiliency does not come easily or naturally after significant trauma. The brain's perceptual processing system is often seriously impacted by trauma and only with time and effort can the negative trajectory be altered. The road to becoming resilient comes through seeking the help and support of others. Having the experience of overcoming adversity in the past can lead to more personal confidence and belief in self. The goal is to help the person develop a positive outlook. For children (and most adults) after traumatic experiences, how to regain a positive outlook must often be taught and does not always come naturally.

While the mental health profession is very aware of negative influences on psychological well-being (Wittstein, 2007; Curry, Wells, Brent, Clarke, Rohde, Albano, Reineke, Benazon & March, 2005), it has paid less attention up to recent times on positive influences. There is growing evidence of a number of positive influences on mental health including: love, intimacy, community, compassion, forgiveness, altruism and service (Ornish 1998; Bernstein, 2003). NRT is a model that incorporates the positive influences as well as addressing negative influences on optimal mental health.

Resiliency is an important response to the stress of living. Stress has long been known to impact the mind, body and spirit depending upon the ability of the person to cope with the stress. Coping is directly related to resiliency and when the individual loses the ability to cope a number of negative consequences can occur including: impacting the developing brain, producing excessive hormonal responses, particularly adrenaline and cortisol, overactivation of the stress response cycle, and a greater vulnerability to medical, psychological and behavioral disorders (McEwen, 2000).

> ## *Gina's Inability to Connect and Make Herself Vulnerable*
>
> *When Gina first arrived in our program, she appeared like the perfect child: no tantrums, following directions the first time, polite with peers, and a good student. The picture that the parents were drawing seemed to fit another child: physical and verbal aggression, sneaky and manipulative behaviors, mean to animals and so on. But soon enough, Gina's problems on an interpersonal level emerged. She was unable to relate to others, did not have the capacity to empathize or share her feelings. Gina had to learn that it was not detrimental or harmful to her survival to expose herself by showing her real self and to make herself vulnerable by expressing her genuine feelings. She learned during her upbringing in an Eastern European orphanage to survive by not needing anyone's attention. Treatment for Gina had to focus on early neglect and the serious impact on her ability to attach to supportive adults. Particularly in a family, she had to learn to take the risk to connect first in small ways then larger, but every risk had to show her brain the connection was better than being alone. Gina grew slowly but surely and improved significantly in attachment skills and as a result of the new support from others her mood issues improved significantly.*
>
> *Femeke Britschgi Cabernard, Ph.D.*

Excessive stress can produce chronic release of cortisol which can produce a series of problems such as altering how the brain functions, specifically in areas of learning and memory, negatively affecting genes by reducing their activation to handling stress and development of insulating myelin, damages the hippocampus resulting in damage to learning, memory and stress regulation (Brunson, Grigoriadi, Lorang & Baram, 2002). Being negatively influenced by stress can start very young in life by being adversely affected by maternal stress during pregnancy which can produce more fearful and more reactive babies (Weinstock, 1997). On the positive side stress need not be the source of negative emotions, it depends on how we experience and handle stress as children and as adults. Mild to moderate stress in childhood has been found to benefit handling stress in adulthood, (Davidson, 2004).

Children do not often learn on their own how to manage stress. In most cases this is a learned behavior based upon attachment with the mother very early in life. If the attachment bond is absent or insufficient, coping with stress can be learned from healing environments that provide treatment for the child (National Scientific Council on the Developing Child, 2005; Johnson, Knitzer & Kaufmann, 2002).

Resiliency is associated with a positive outlook as well as positive pursuits such as the following: counting your blessings, performing acts of kindness, being thankful, forgiving others, spending time and energy with family, taking care of your body, and developing coping strategies for stress (Lyubomirsky, King & Diener, 2005). Resiliency and attachment are both key factors in coping with and bouncing back from stressful and even traumatic experiences in life. With strong attachments and a resilient orientation to living, the result can be not just getting by in life but developing optimal mental health.

Optimum Mental Health

The goal of Neurological Reparative Therapy is to promote optimal mental health. In the past the term mental health was often avoided in psychology. The problem was the belief that the general public translated mental health to mean services for the insane or "crazy people." To an extent this was true because it has always been more socially acceptable to have a physical problem than a mental one. The roots of such thinking likely come from the mystery surrounding the workings of the brain and the fear people have of being able to heal from mental problems. However the reluctance to consider mental health is decreasing as health in all respects has become mainstream, and being healthy of mind is getting the recognition of being every bit as important as other types of health.

But what does it mean to be mentally healthy? If psychology and psychiatry strive to promote optimum mental health, it would help to have a clear understanding of what this concept means. There have been a number of operational definitions of mental health over time. For centuries the opposite of mental health was insanity, which could mean anything from hearing voices, to seeing visions, to having any experience of "reality" other than the mainstream point of view. However mainstream is a reference point and culturally defined. As such, some cultures allowed more divergence and uniqueness in lifestyle, personal expression and perception of "reality," and other cultures not so much. Having a definition of sanity or mental health that was based upon cultural norms posed some serious issues. In some cultures you might kiss a police officer as a normal greeting, try this in New York and you may find yourself behind bars in either a jail or 'mental ward.' A common term in the American culture is someone going "mental." This does not refer to someone showing good mental health but the opposite such as losing control of "reality," a term meaning what most people perceive and experience. Of the many cultures of the world, our western culture has one of the more rigid definitions of the range of what is considered reality.

As recently as the 1980s, one of the most popular psychological instruments to identify mental disorders asked a variety of questions related to religious experiences. The revision of the MMPI dropped all such questions because it had to reflect a change in our view of insanity from someone who might experience oneness with Jesus Christ in meditation to someone who was stuck in believing he was Jesus Christ all the time. In this example, sanity was not based upon a common experience of reality as much as it was based upon the flexibility to move in and out of a variety of experiences.

In a myriad of ways society has attempted to define mental health as a mainstream or common experience of the world. Of course the problem with legislating reality is that we all experience the world quite differently and this is actually mentally healthy. There have always been problems with defining mental health as having the same views and feelings as most people. For example, four decades ago Alan Watts in his lecture "The Value of Psychotic Experience" (Watts, 1960) points out that in the middle ages religion was taken very seriously and anyone who wavered from the dogmatic position of the time might experience the inquisition or other attempts to forcefully return the person back into the mainstream. Watts believed religion was taken much less seriously in the modern world and he viewed the new 'religion' as psychiatry, which he observed was taken very seriously by our culture. Watts observed that in this new religion the temples are hospitals, the priests are psychiatrists with vestments (white coats) and there is even sacramental communion (psychotropic drugs). Therefore if someone were to stray from the dogmatic position of mainstream psychiatric experience, the result might be involuntary confinement in a "mental health" ward until the person was, at times painfully, forced back into mainstream experiences. The point Watts makes is that we need people around us to be different so we ourselves don't get rigidly stuck in our own version of "reality." While somewhat extreme, just the way Alan Watts liked his examples, there is some truth to his observation. Fortunately there is more tolerance currently for different experiences of the world in professional circles, but there is still a theme in our society that anyone who dances to the beat of a different drummer is "not right in the head" and it may be best to avoid such unpredictable people.

If a common experience of reality is not a good indicator of mental health, then what is? A more balanced definition of optimal mental health does not rely on experience but on a combination of mental faculties that allow an individual to adapt and engage with the world. These faculties include neurological specialization, mental flexibility, and overall mental coordination that moves the individual toward healing, health and thriving in life. We now believe that the brain is not only focused on surviving but it also has an internal draw toward happiness or thriving (Diener & Biswas-Diener, 2008). This internal drive toward health and thriving can help internal adaptations of the brain during the therapeutic process, such as the following:

Regions of the brain specialize, enhancing complexity—the healthy brain is one where the many regions have developed advanced and sophisticated complexity. Optimal capacities come from such complexity within brain regions. Over a very long evolutionary history, the brain has grown in diversity and specificity of its many parts. For example, most human brains have a highly developed visual cortex in the occipital lobe. The more this region of the brain is used, the more complex it becomes due to the growth and development promoted by continuous use. In experiments where the visual center of the brain has been left unstimulated it does not take long before the cortex begins to deteriorate and the brain adapts to a new circumstance. Healthy neurons are like healthy muscles, they work best when they are exercised and trained to do work.

Mental flexibility—the brain is prepared to adapt and change course at all stages of life. This ability could be considered mental flexibility. Mental flexibility is less about the ability of the brain to change than it is the overall brain coordination that will set the priorities of what the brain regions will focus on. Mental flexibility could be viewed as a natural state for the brain. In this way the brain's natural state includes flexibility and mental health. There are many factors that frequently interrupt the brain's ability to be flexible and adapt to new challenges. Adverse impacts on flexibility can come from brain damage, external chemical assaults, internal chemical imbalances, traumatic stress, poor attachment, and a large number of influences that rob the brain of mental flexibility and positive mental health.

The human mind moves naturally toward healing, health and thriving—based upon the innate desire of the brain to survive and thrive, it will move toward positive growth and development unless negative forces block this internal drive. Therefore the healthy brain in every situation is using its considerable abilities to perceive, understand, adapt and influence the world. Being able to put your personal stamp on your personal experience is one important aspect of personal contentment. It is the mind that uses the many abilities of the brain to promote healing, health and happiness or personal contentment.

Neuro-integration requires that the complex brain must work as a collaborative whole—it is of little use to the brain to have highly developed and sophisticated regions if there is a lack of internal coordination. Due to the immense power of the human brain to take in and process sensory input, without coordination of focus and attention it would soon be a symphony orchestra where all the instruments were playing a different score—resulting in total chaos. The primary coordinator of the brain is the orbitofrontal cortex in the prefrontal region of the brain. The brain can be compared to a sports team; it is not always the team with the best individual talent that prevails, but the one that is the most cohesive in using the individual players to form a synergy where the whole is greater than the sum of its parts. The brain without coordination and synergy is not an optimally healthy brain.

A place where many sciences come together is in a general agreement that what a person perceives becomes their own personal reality. This is the basis for cognitive behavioral therapy and its predecessor, rational emotive therapy. Several internal contributors go into personal perception such as: history and experience, enculturation, mood, exposure to information, and many other contributing factors. What is clear is that the way I perceive something becomes my reality, whether it is consistent with others or not. Therefore perception is a critical component of optimal mental health because what we perceive is what we consider our reality. It is possible to find mentally healthy people in prisons and in war zones and find people with little mental health in affluent suburbs and elite country clubs. Our experience of life has less to do with objective reality and a great deal to do with our perception of our world.

Perception is heavily based upon our internal view of the world which was called our inner working model in attachment literature (Bowlby, 1982). Our model of the world was heavily influenced by both nature and nurture and a trajectory of experience was set in place very early in life. Perception is influenced from the outside but it is primarily an internal process. Because so much of the world around us is defined inside of our brain, effective treatment must impact perception.

Perceptual differences among people can create challenges. The court system has long struggled with a strange fact that several witnesses can experience the same event and have different descriptions. How is this possible, and how could two witnesses who watched a hit and run accident where one saw a blue Ford and the other a green Nissan both pass a polygraph test? The answer is that each of the witnesses was telling the truth, but it turns out their truth is subjective rather than objective truth. Each person had a perception that is a combination of sensory input coming through the optic nerve and processed by the brain's visual cortex (known as Area 17) in the occipital lobe. The visual sensory input is then processed in relationship to past experiences with similar events resulting in what the person believes he or she observed. But our experience is heavily influenced by our past experiences. We know that direct visual experience can be quite flawed and the car in question may turn out to not be what either of the witnesses believed they saw. The point here is that perception is less about objective reality and more about an internal assessment influenced by past events, all used to process new experiences.

Much like observing an accident, the events that take place around us each day are completely subject to our perception of what happened, why it happened, and the significance of the situation. As in perceiving a car that was never involved in the event, our perceptions can be faulty in each of these areas—the what, the why and the importance of any situation. A person might misunderstand what really happened, what caused it to happen and believe it is either more or less important in the scheme of things than it actually is. The last part is critically important because in a very real way, what we perceive to be a reality becomes our reality. Now we must move from an external event like the car accident to our experience of life around us. Our understanding of events processed by our past experience becomes our perceptual system. How we perceive events in our life has a great deal to say about how we feel about the events and how we choose to respond or react to these events. Because of the way the brain works, what we perceive is what we experience.

There is an obvious connection between our perceptions of the world around us and our own mental health. That connection is that we all live not as much in the objective reality of the world around us but in our inner perceptions of this world. There are extremely wealthy individuals who worry they do not have enough money, there are amazing athletes who feel like a failure unless they finish first every time, and many years ago the woman some people think was the most beautiful person of her era, Marilyn Monroe, took her own life in part because she did not feel beautiful on the inside or on the outside. In each case it is the perception rather than the objective reality that the person experienced. Living in the world of our perceptual schema is not only true in the extreme cases mentioned above, it is true for each of us.

The expression is often repeated that someone needs a 'reality check.' This is true of everyone throughout life because our internal perceptions seldom match objective reality, particularly if stress comes into play. Under stress brilliant individuals can feel ignorant, uniquely skilled individuals can feel incompetent, and some of the world's most remarkable individuals: Abraham Lincoln, Mohandas Gandhi, Martin Luther King, Jr. and Agnesë Gonxhe Bojaxh (Mother Teresa) have felt like failures. The reason for this is the individual's perceptual system. We all need reality checks because for each of us the reality we live is inexorably linked to our internal perceptions.

Misperceptions can obviously go in both directions, understating one's skill or impact on others or overstating who and what we are. When an individual goes to an extreme in either direction, this is often a symptom of a mental health problem. In fact one of the most frequent mental health problems in adults is alternating going to extremes in both directions, a characteristic of bi-polar disorder. One of the primary tasks of a mental health professional is to provide a very personal reality check for the client. To help the young adult who has been rejected by a love interest see that there are reasons to go on living, to help the manic person see that their grandiose beliefs are exaggerated and temporary, as are the depressive beliefs that will soon follow. These examples may be extreme, but it is a characteristic of human beings to overcorrect, to focus on one event rather than the big picture. Optimal mental health requires a balanced perspective and an openness to external reality checks all around us. In this way perception is directly linked to mental health and the role of the therapist, to a large extent, is a facilitator of that balanced perspective and a perceptual system that incorporates external reality checks.

Optimal mental health also requires the individual to handle the emotions that are generated in daily life. There are a number of components of emotional health including: understanding personal feeling states, accurately perceiving feeling states in others, managing strong feelings, developing empathy, and using emotions to enhance relationship connections with others (Denham, 1998). None of these abilities comes naturally and each must be learned. Promoting mental health requires a setting where each of these abilities must be on the curriculum.

Optimal mental health also takes advantage of the individual's capacity for self-healing. This capacity is nothing short of amazing. We do not question our body's ability to physically heal itself without the need for us to give the healing our undivided attention. A paper cut or a bruise caused by running into a kitchen counter will both heal quite well without any intentional step on our part. The body knows what to do, we just need to avoid preventing it from doing its job. Our emotions are very much the same. The brain is the master healer and we are just beginning to learn what pharmaceutical firms have known for some time. Although drug manufacturers have huge advertising budgets that encourage all of us to "Ask your doctor" about their new drug, they do not encourage you to ask about your brain's ability to heal without the need for medication. An excellent case in point is the "Placebo Effect" or what is starting to be known as the "Placebo Response" (Benedetti, Mayberg, Wagner, Stohler & Zubieta, 2005).

The Placebo Response is a specific description of how the brain heals the physical and emotional insults of life. This is a clear departure from the historical view that the placebo effect is the "non-specific cure," faux or sham cure or even a "nuisance" usually associated with the use of a sugar pill. The phenomenon has long been associated more with gullibility or trickery then innate self-healing. However, we are learning much more about the Placebo Response and what it can produce and how this occurs. This process is how the brain signals the rest of the body to heal by including the internal pharmacy of the body to address whatever the concern may be from pain, to depression, to anxiety, to over-activity and much more. What we call pain is a combination of sensory inputs to the brain combined with our internal perceptual orientation. The brain has pain "control gates" that let in or shut out the sensory inputs (Wagner, Rilling, Smith, Sokolik, Casey, Davidson, Kosslyn, Rose & Cohen, 2004). Therefore pain can be impacted by perception and by release of internal analgesics. Two examples are the internal release of opioids to reduce pain and relax parts of the body, such as respiration and blood pressure, and dopamine, a biochemical substance released by the frontal cortex of the brain that is associated with improved sense of well-being, enhanced cognitive acuity, improved body functioning, such as sleep and digestion, and reducing the stress response cycle (Benedetti, et. al., 2005).

The key to the individual's ability is the brain. It turns out that the brain can often do quite well in self-healing without the use of sophisticated and expensive pharmaceuticals, and the drug companies have known this for many years. Since the 1940s medical science has recognized the phenomenon of patients improving not from anything from without but entirely from healing coming from within. An article appeared in one of the top medical journals in 1955 called "The Powerful Placebo" (Beecher, 1955). While this information was used to improve the process of developing and testing drugs, it has also had a darker history when the body's ability to self-heal was quickly withheld because of the potential to impact pharmaceutical profits.

A number of facts related to the Placebo Effect have received little or no attention, for example, the brain has shown repeatedly that it can do better without drugs than with them (Kaptchuk, 1998), research showing the body's ability to heal is superior to medications has been carefully guarded by drug companies, and the Placebo Effect has been growing stronger over the years (Silberman, 2009). It also turns out that the Placebo Response is not consistent and is impacted by location, culture, and varies by individuals. It has also been found that the color of the placebo and its shape can make a difference (Silberman, 2009). In fact the effectiveness of some medications may be directly related to the advertising of the manufacturer and how well they produce a positive expectation in the patient taking the drug.

If a patient believes she will improve and this jumpstarts inner self-healing, then the reverse should be true that the belief that she will not improve should have negative outcomes. Research has shown this to be true and this process is known as the Nocebo Effect (Benneditti, et. al., 2005).

The intrigue with this issue and drug companies, while interesting, is of less importance than the fact that the brain has been shown in medical research to have amazing curative abilities. Rather than hide this from the public, it is time to train people to use their innate abilities through interventions such as positive thinking, relaxation training, meditation, visualization, strength-based interventions and many other tools to unleash inner healing. Optimizing internal healing potential is an important component of optimal mental health.

Because the brain is complex beyond our current understanding (it has yet to fully understand itself), there is a risk to having the tool more powerful and sophisticated than the craftsman. It is actually not very difficult or unusual for the power of the brain to overwhelm the individual. We use expressions like 'she was overcome with her emotions' or 'he was so angry he lost control' or 'that person just can't handle his or her own thoughts, urges, successes, failures, or _____ (fill in the blank). In these cases the brain is a vehicle so powerful that the operator can't stay in control. Throughout our lives we need the help of others to understand what is going on inside of us. There is little chance that we can develop this insight independent of others throughout our lives. This is one reason that socially successful people are better adjusted, show more personal contentment and live longer lives.

Socially successful people begin life drawing on the many positive aspects of a secure attachment with a biological mother (in most cases). The positive results are better self-awareness, internal self-regulation and internal healing, self-confidence, more positive outlook, a more balanced inner working model (perceptual framework), and ability to handle the stress of living and bounce back from the inevitable struggles of life (resiliency).

Related to the help the healthy individual gets from others is the need for an internal regulator or chief executive officer (CEO) of the brain. With literally millions of operations occurring all the time, recent research is finding that when the brain is at rest it is still profoundly active, there must be a pilot of the ship or the individual will be overwhelmed by the brain rather than taking advantage of what the brain can do to help the person. A decision-maker inside the brain must be able to prioritize, focus, ignore some inputs and highlight others. Without the area in the prefrontal region of the brain, called the orbitofrontal cortex, acting as the CEO or decision- maker, the result can be chaos in multiple areas. As we grow in our understanding of the brain it is not surprising that the capacity and operations of the human brain can overwhelm some individuals. It actually is somewhat surprising when individuals demonstrate significant control and the ability to harness the power and abilities of the brain. At any moment in life the brain can become a runaway train taking us where we would rather not go. This most often is experienced as our emotions hijacking us, but emotions are an outgrowth of our perceptions. Mental flexibility, emotional control, a balanced perceptual system, and our internal ability to heal mental and emotional wounds are all required aspects of mental health and all depend upon the orbitofrontal cortex to take the reins of the brain.

The Brain's Information Processing System

Perception is only one component of the functioning brain. The brain also has multiple other components including: sensory intake and analysis, metabolic processes, memory storage and retrieval, activation and deactivation among a few examples. The brain is taking in thousands of sensory inputs and processing them at all times, both when the individual is in what we consider the awake state and during the deepest sleep. New information is showing that the brain actually never sleeps and is processing around the clock. A practical definition of the mind includes the central receiving and processing system of the brain. The mind makes meaning of the inputs it decides to focus on from among the many alternative thoughts and feelings coming into awareness.

Brain processes can be either automatic requiring no focus awareness, such as the brain stem regulating body temperature, heart rate and respiration, or on the other end of the continuum it can process the most sophisticated math or phenomenological problem or concept. Somewhere in the middle of the processing continuum is the brain's protective mechanism to respond to external threats, which is partially automatic and partially within our awareness. For higher order reasoning to occur the brain needs a chief executive officer to make some decisions in all this complexity. The decision-maker of the brain is found in the prefrontal cortex and is called the orbitofrontal cortex.

The brain's processing system is highly influenced by both early attachment and by traumatic experiences throughout life. In both cases all incoming sensory input will be processed through the limbic region of the brain and will be compared to past stressful events. When a child has less than a strong bond with a primary care provider, the world is a threatening place and the child's ability to self-regulate and manage internal stress are both severely impacted. In a similar way, traumatic experiences impact the brain with a heightened sense of awareness to perceived threats and an inability to cope with the stress response cycle that is generated. In both of these cases the limbic region combines traumatic memories with a sense of feeling overwhelmed while the child has the inability to cope with the results. In these cases the brain's information processing system is creating a habitual stress cycle that will create serious problems for the individual in the short and long run, possibly including medical disease and early death (Felitti, Anda, Nordenberg, Williamson, Spitz, Edwards & Koss, 1998). Due to the fact that most children with serious mental health issues have a history of poor attachment and/or traumatic experience, the brain's information processing system must be impacted as a part of healing and treatment. The change must move the processing from primarily the limbic region to primarily the prefrontal cortex.

The Neurology of Community

Great focus in most traditional therapies goes into building the self. If a person has little sense of a self then he or she goes through life buffeted by events and conditions in the environment with little internal ability to manage life. However, as important as the self, the internal narrative is there is a growing acknowledgement of the importance of the larger self or being connected and a part of something greater than the self. Because of this it has become increasingly important that psychological therapies not only enhance the personal self but also the intrapersonal self or the awareness of being connected to others (also called attachment). The focus on the self and the focus on the other cannot be mutually exclusive. We learn about ourselves from the interactions with others and we learn empathy and understanding of others by going within ourselves and expanding that to others. In the same way, the neuronal activity for both these directions is very similar.

The orientation of the brain in structure and in function is not solitary but strives for connections, it has an awareness of being separate from others but it defines itself in relationship to others. We are tall or short based not on an objective measure but upon the height of those around us. We measure ourselves in many ways based upon our contact with others. The brain has instinctual drives to connect with others, which in a way is similar to the internal process of neurons driven to find each other, form families, and live a long life. Without this connection with other neurons, instead of a long life the neuron may have a very short life indeed. Connection is life for the neuron and connection is life for the brain itself.

Our first instinctual drive is to bond and attach to a care provider who literally holds our life in her/his hands. Unless the newborn finds a source of safety, nourishment, warmth and connection within minutes of birth, the brain knows that continued existence is at serious risk. The brain knows this not from a developed reasoning center but through an instinctive drive instilled through genetic coding. The instinctual drives in the developing brain do not like risks and have genetic and evolutionary protections from serious survival risks. Only the genes of survivors are passed on to the next generation and over scores of generations the brain knows both avoidance of threats and specific ways to adapt to threats. The most fundamental protection from threats is attachment with a primary source for our basic needs. We do not need to teach a newborn to display attachment behaviors, this is instinctively driven. When the attachment process works correctly, the mother responds to the child with instinctively driven bonding behaviors. Therefore the first act of the newborn is to reach out to someone outside of the self and if this process is successful this drive to reach out to others will continue throughout the lifespan.

The word community comes from the Latin word for "common" as in having something in common with each other. What a child and an adult have in common with each other and with the community in which they live is life itself. For the newborn child, life is directly connected to the care provider. From the first minutes and days of life, the human being must quickly become part of something greater than the self, their very survival depends on it. This neurological process predisposes us to be communal animals in that for us to survive and to thrive connection with others is required.

The brain has a variety of ways it promotes connection. In the early process of migration neurons move around in the undeveloped brain searching for other neurons to connect with and do work together. In this way the neuron can be called a social cell because like the total organism, unless the single neuron finds a family, a home and a community, it will die. From the first minutes of life the process of connection is going on both internal to the brain and external to the environment. This instinctual process has been called a drive to move from a 'me' to a 'we' through life (Siegel, 2010). In fact the experience of the we comes before the sense of me. The newborn's eyesight will need to quickly develop the ability to imprint the unique face of the primary care provider. The child's other senses will be directed to identify smell, taste, sound and the touch of the source of safety and comfort. The child's instincts look to reestablish the connection that has been in place for the first nine months in the womb. The very first experiences of life are of connection to more than the individual or separate self and the rest of the child's life will parallel this process of looking for connection and thriving or not based upon the outcome of this search.

There is an early neurological process that promotes and accomplishes connection or attachment. The left hemisphere is more developed early in childhood to promote attachment functions with the primary care provider, usually the mother. There are areas of the brain that enable attachment that are called bonding or resonance centers. The early development of the prefrontal cortex enables attachment and the insula and anterior cingulated cortex are primary players. There are mirror neurons in these areas of the brain that function as receivers of the messages sent by the mother for comfort, soothing, and an overall sense of safety. As the attachment with the mother grows and develops successfully, a whole range of very good things happen for the child — safety and security is established, stress management is learned as is self-regulation, management of the central nervous system is an outgrowth and a primitive level of confidence in coping with the stresses of living. Attachment will provide much of what the child will need to buffer the negative impacts of stress and anxiety throughout life and attachment is a connection with another or what could be called something greater than self or the larger self. As in the womb, successful early childhood experiences are based upon a sense of being connected to a larger self and the rest of the individual's life will continue this drive toward connection and community.

Just as positive attachment with a primary care provider facilities essential components of early brain health, later connection with an expanding community likewise promotes the health of the developing brain. As the social network expands so does the prefrontal cortex. The development of these internal and external components promotes further ingredients to health such as understanding and managing emotions, regulating behavior, mental and affective flexibility, and over time the essential components of the higher order reasoning centers producing executive functions. The process of the expansion of the external environment assisting the growth of the internal brain development further links the individual with something greater than the self.

It is fair to say that there is only a 'self' in the context of the 'other' and throughout most of life the self and the other are at times indistinguishable. Examples include the mother/child bond, the influence of the family on how the child perceives the world, the impact of peers on perceptions and even the lifelong journey of many to find spiritual ways to become one with the beloved, which is a fundamental principle of every major spiritual tradition. But individuals do develop a sense of the individual self or what could be called the small self. Healthy individuals will also develop throughout life the sense of the large self or the expanded network of the self connected to family, peers, neighborhood, and spiritual networks of the family of man and a higher power or creator.

All developmental periods of life are defined by social networks. Early on it is the mother/child bond, then the father comes into the picture and the family unit is the network that provides the child with the foundational skills of surviving and thriving within a protective community structure. As the child grows older there is often an extended family network that becomes involved and optimally the protective structure of the family expands to include more adults and children in an expanding arc of social connection, skill development and thriving. The child soon experiences day care, pre-school and then full school days, usually away from the family. When this is successful, the protective network for the child continues to expand to include a safe place to learn and play (the two primary jobs of a child) in a larger school community. As the child ages peers begin to become important and can expand the sense of connection even further. In this way the child has an expanding network of connection that corresponds to very important internal brain and body changes. Thriving in life takes place in both an internal and external framework promoting a healthy individual through healthy attachments to an ever growing support community.

Both the neurobiology of attachment and of community are fundamental to the development of a healthy brain. There are many ways these processes can be disrupted. Such things as loss, neglect, abuse, serious medical disease, and insecure bonding among other examples can set the stage for a life-long battle with internal and external disorders. Just as the successful attachment with a primary care provider and an expanding community enables thriving, the lack of successful connection can result in the most serious threats to optimal mental health. The physiology and psychology of the human being is based upon interconnection, and connection will be the most important factor leading to success or distress throughout the individual's lifespan.

In this chapter the science behind Neurological Reparative Therapy has been briefly provided. As each of the main concepts have been discussed, overlap and redundancy are apparent. This is why optimal mental health has been described as a weave of related factors that promote the individual's ability to thrive in a world full of stress and, at times, unpredictable events requiring us to learn to cope. With the understanding of brain science, attachment, trauma and resiliency, we can now turn the attention to how optimal mental health can be promoted in a therapeutic process.

The Foundations of NRT

The literature and research base of NRT is extensive and covers multiple disciplines.

Although still early in our understanding of the brain, Brain Science is already opening doors.

Trauma literature is clear about how the brain adapts and what must be addressed for recovery.

Attachment research indicates the essential nature of connecting with others for healthy functioning.

Resiliency literature points to the tools for repairing the body and the brain.

Positive Psychology builds on strengths rather than focuses on deficiencies, including unleashing the brain's innate ability to self heal.

Brain's processing system must change from the reactive limbic system to the prefrontal cortex.

Neurobiology of community—the brain must learn to connect with other brains.

Chapter

4

The Five Goals of Neurological Reparative Therapy

With the foundations of Neurological Reparative Therapy briefly covered in Chapter 3, the specifics of the approach can now be addressed. Because the research and literature foundations of this model cover multiple disciplines within psychology, integration will be a critical factor. Integration will be an important component of drawing on the disciplines of brain science, trauma treatment, attachment, and resiliency. Integration within the model is symbolic of the importance of integration within the brain in how it processes information and makes decisions. Finally, integration will be stressed when treatment interventions are developed to include as many aspects of the child's environment as possible. As an overall statement, Neurological Reparative Therapy can be said to be an integrative model.

Neurotransformation

The overall goal of NRT is positive brain change or neurotransformation. Transforming the most complex organic structure known to man is complex but we are beginning to have a richer understanding of how this process works and it can be supported. Brain change has moved from science fiction to science fact. Unexplained psychiatric improvements of the past are now understood to be the result of positive adaptations of the living, changing and ever transforming brain. Neurological conditions once thought to be permanent have now been shown to be changeable through neurotransformation. Positive brain changes have shown significant improvement in conditions as diverse as: strokes, learning disabilities, cognitive deficiencies and IQ, memory in seniors, obsessive compulsive disorder, traumatic experiences, visual acuity, autism, paralysis, pain management, cerebral palsy, spinal cord injuries, Parkinson's, multiple sclerosis, arthritis and many other conditions formally viewed as permanent (Doidge, 2007).

At least four types of neurotransformation have been identified, including:

1. Neural map expansion — with experience, neuron firing and learning, the neural maps expand within the brain.

2. Sensory reassignment — when one of the senses is damaged or restricted other senses can step-up to provide the brain additional input, such as when blindness can enhance auditory acuity.

3. Alternative strategies — the brain can figure out new ways to accomplish a task following impairment.

4. Region reassignment — when one region of the brain is prevented from doing its function, other regions can assume this function (Grafman & Litvan, 1999).

Each of the above forms of neurotransformation can help individuals to develop positive adaptations to injuries or deficiencies within the brain. The issue of traumatic experience is of particular interest when working in mental health settings with children, teens and adults. The role of the limbic region of the brain in traumatic memory is well known, as is the hypersensitivity of limbic structures following trauma. We now know that the amygdala (reactive fear center) and the hypothalamus (stress activation and memory) can adjust in positive ways following a traumatic experience. The brain simply needs to be trained in more adaptive responses. Other parts of the limbic region can provide internal rewards through pleasurable chemical signals that can promote learning and changing in positive adaptation. The brain simply needs to be trained to do this.

There are functional reasons why the brain develops negative adaptations to injury such as traumatic experiences. The main purpose of limbic reactivity is to insure life threatening experiences are avoided in the future. The hypothalamus is involved in taking short-term memory and turning it into long-term memory. The ability of the brain's long-term memory is proving to be more substantial than previously believed, shown in research where infants aged 1 and 2 years store facts and events in memory (Bauer, 2005). When this occurs the neurons change in size and shape and increase synaptic connections within the brain (Kandel, 2003). Therefore the brain may not be inclined to change without prompting and assistance from the outside. Positive brain adaptation is a function of two steps, the first is 1. to learn more functional adaptive responses and the second is to unlearn non-adaptive reactions. Treatment of traumatic 2. disorders must involve both steps. Positive adaptations can be taught through a variety of interventions that will be discussed in the next few chapters. The brain assists with unlearning by activating neuromodulators that assist in wiping away unneeded neural connections. An example of unlearning is the process of recovering from grief when a loved one dies and is no longer present, eliminating desired contact and interactions. The brain must unlearn the expectation of such contact and must learn that things must now change (Rosenzweig, Barnes & McNaughton,

2002). Depending upon the strength of the attachment, this unlearning process can be very slow and painful.

The brain is designed to change in part through the help of nerve growth factor or brain derived growth factor (BDGF). It is the function of BDGFs to: 1. Wire neurons together when they fire, 2. Promote myelin growth making neurons faster and more efficient, 3. Turn on the nucleus basalis to promote sustained focus and attention, and 4. Shut down during critical periods to encode the learning in memory and prevent competing influences (Fagiolini & Hensch, 2000). In other words, BDGFs make us smarter by first adding to the number of neurons and synapses and second, increasing attention within the brain; attention is synonymous with brain growth. The final role of BDGFs regarding shutting down during critical periods may help explain autism because when the brain releases massive amounts of BDGFs early on in a critical period, the transformation of the brain is shut down too early leaving neuronal connections undifferentiated and producing such autism symptoms as hyper-excitability, hypersensitive sensory responses and other symptoms of pervasive developmental disorder (Rubenstein & Merzenich, 2003).

Positive brain change has attracted a host of dubious strategies based upon poor research. Everything from diet to brain exercises to a variety of drugs. The desire to promote positive brain change and enhance neurotransformation is ever present in popular press, for example, the cover story of Newsweek magazine as I was writing this chapter. The answer to the Newsweek question as to what actually produces positive brain change comes down to: 1. Consistent aerobic and resistance exercise is known to be one of the best brain building strategies, 2. Mindfulness meditation that relaxes the body reducing stress while enhancing attention and concentration, and 3. Mental activities that challenge decision-making, mental agility, focused attention, and cognitive flexibility (Begley & Yarett, 2011). There is considerable research that supports these three pillars of improved brain growth and functioning. Any program designed to promote neurotransformation and positive brain change will be built upon these three important components.

The brain's ability to transform itself is not all good news. The same brain functions that allow change due to the impact of experience are the same functions that reinforce habitual perceptions and reactions. If the brain consistently fires an array of neural networks, these networks grow, expand and became the pathways of choice. If a person who struggles with obsessive compulsive disorder consistently counts to three before performing any task, the networks involved become stronger with every repetition. The function of treatment is to promote new neural pathways while unlearning and moving beyond non-adaptive pathways. One model of treatment to do this is Neurological Reparative Therapy.

The Five Goals of NRT

The best starting place to explain Neurological Reparative Therapy as a treatment model is to consider the goals to be achieved. There are five primary goals of NRT that are general in nature and are not necessarily sequential. The sequential steps of the model will be found in the next chapter. Each step of the process addresses one or more of the goals. The combination of the goals and steps constitute the ten premises of Neurological Reparative Therapy.

1. Facilitate perceptual changes of the self, others and the child's inner working model

The individual's experience in life is directly connected to his or her perceptions based upon the inner working model or how the person interprets what he or she experiences. Based upon the individual's perceptions, cognitive mental maps plot a course the individual will travel through life, including how the person typically feels and behaves. Feelings and behaviors are important in this context because these observable issues are what the practitioner is called upon to help change. While other treatment models focus on behaviors, NRT begins with a focus on how the brain perceives the self, others and the environment. The first goal is to impact perceptions by altering cognitions for the purpose of providing a more positive and optimistic orientation rather than a negative and depressive mind set—issues found in many clients with disturbances of emotions. Therapeutic work is directed toward developing a sense of self-efficacy and helping the individual view others as resources for support and assistance, this overlaps with the focus on attachment.

The last chapter discussed the importance of perceptions. Optimal mental health has less to do with the people, conditions and events in a person's life than the individual's perceptions of the people, conditions and events. It is very good news that the individual has the internal ability to alter perceptions and therefore alter his or her life experience. The tendency for people who face a difficult situation is to believe there is only one way they are capable of perceiving the situation and it is often negative. When difficult events happen we have choices in how we view the situation and how we respond. Some individuals are more resilient in the face of adversity while others respond to difficulty by feeling overwhelmed or even defeated. The process of NRT is to open the mind up to additional possibilities and help individuals see they have the internal ability to view a situation in the way they choose to. For example, the loss of a significant relationship may either be perceived as devastating or viewed as temporarily difficult but for the best in the long run. In a child's world, a cancelled visit with a family member can either be perceived as a significant loss or an undesirable change in schedule that opens some time to do something enjoyable. The difference is the child's perception of the event, and perceptions are subject to the person's control.

For people who have histories of trauma, perceptions are heavily influenced by the hippocampus and amygdala of the limbic region of the brain. Negative experiences of the past connect to experiences in the present—a dynamic that can result in posttraumatic stress disorder (PTSD) and other mood disorders. When the person is stuck in the dynamics of PTSD and other disorders, there will be little or no recognition that the experience is being altered by perceptions. At such times the person believes his or her feelings and behaviors are simply a direct result of the situation with no ability to exercise a personal sense of control whatsoever. When the brain processes situations in this way, the prefrontal cortex has little involvement and therefore the executive functions of the individual are put to minimal use. It is the idle executive functions that can be the source of the internal ability of the individual to consider other possible explanations, alternatives, and/or responses to events. When post-traumatic perceptions impair or shut down executive functions of the individual, it takes assistance from the outside, quite literally thinking for the individual, to provide the ability to see a bigger picture than the one the limbic brain is confined to based upon past traumatic experiences.

The critically important intervention of helping the individual change perceptions may be challenging to successfully accomplish, but the process is not particularly complex. Parents and teachers do this all the time with children. The process is to get the child's attention, have the child relax as much as possible, and the adult connects with the child's higher order reasoning centers by discussing, explaining or showing the child a new approach to the situation. When the child launches into a tantrum at the news his family must cancel a visit, the adult can begin by soothing the child, allowing feelings to be expressed and letting the child know that you are there to support him or her. When possible the adult can talk to the child and explain the visit was rescheduled and will take place at a future time. The adult can point out the possible activities that can now take place instead of the visit that the child enjoys. When the adult provides these alternative perceptions and higher order reasoning to the situation, the child's prefrontal cortex will be stimulated from the outside and therefore the adult is literally exercising the executive functions for the child and developing new neural maps within the child's brain.

The inner working model of the child is not just a function of reactive perceptions, it also includes a sense of self and how the individual sees himself or herself in relation to others and to the world. For many children with a traumatic history, the inner working model of the self is negative. The sense of self may even be characterized by self-loathing and self-hatred. When a child is seriously neglected, the internal experience is that he or she is not worthy of being treated better. At times physically abused children perceive they deserved how they were abused and possibly deserved worse treatment. Abandoned children can come to believe it was some type of inadequacy on their part that the parent needed to get away from.

The perception of responsibility for abuse is often experienced as the child's not the adult's. The resulting inner working model can be generalized to: *I am not worth the love of a mother, I deserved the beatings I received, and I was bad because I had sexual contact with Uncle Jim and I even liked it.* Because these types of traumas are highly covert, as opposed to trauma coming from an overt event such as an accident or medical procedure, the inner working model of the child may spin out of control building one faulty perception upon another. *'I deserved the beating because I spilled the milk'* can become an inner working model that *'I am someone who never does anything right. I was involved in the sexual abuse so I am a bad person in all respects.'* In the absence of thoughtful consideration of such perceptions, they can turn into beliefs through repetitive thinking. The individual's inner working model of the self can become amazingly negative.

Inner working models are also very important in how the child perceives his or her role in connection with others. Everyone learns about themselves through the responses they receive from the outside. Children who are not cared for in families develop a belief they do not fit in with others. Children who are harmed in relationships learn to avoid vulnerability around others. Children who were molested try to either blend into the background and not be noticed, or they may do the opposite and act out sexually, believing sexual abuse is inevitable but they want some control in what happens and when it happens. Just as with perceptions of the self, the inner working model of how the child views his or her role with other people must often be altered from the outside due to how internally engrained the faulty perceptions are.

The best way for a child to develop a positive sense of self or a positive connection with others is to have a direct experience. The brain changes based upon experiences. Over time the brain must form new neural networks of a new inner working model if the negative model is to be replaced. It is important to start small and help the individual, particularly a child, experience small amounts of success. Even with small successes the child may think it was a mistake or due to someone else and not take credit for a job well done. For the inner working model of a healthy self, the individual needs to perceive some level of competence, influence, cognitive skill, personal control or some other experience that is different than the default model that comes to the surface repeatedly. Small successes can expand to larger successes.

 Much too often adults seek large gains and much quicker than the child's brain can manage. Our culture is an impatient one where we want quick successes. When an adult tells a child, "I have told you many times to tell the truth, why can't you be honest with me?" Such a statement from a brain perspective is like saying, "I have shown you several times how to type on the keyboard with your eyes closed, why can't you do it?" The brain functions from the mental maps it creates from experience and from its internal perceptions. It takes time and repetition to change these maps and no pleading and expressions of frustration will speed up the brain, in fact, such approaches are likely to delay changes in the brain.

The individual must experience some successes, however small they may be in the beginning. The person must experience making a positive impact, having some positive influence on others, and is helped by a supportive adult to begin to see the world as a more friendly and nurturing place than he or she believes. An example would be to help a child see school as a fun place to learn rather than a scary place where social and academic problems produce failure.

In summary, the key concepts for goal number one are:

- Facilitate a perception change
- Build a positive inner working model of self and others
- Focus on small successes leading to larger successes
- Repetition of all of the above to enable neurological change

The following are some ways to work on changing the child's inner working model:

1. Tell me at least five adults you can go to when you need support and help.

2. Today in our session we are going to make a list of all the things you are good at; let's see how long the list is.

3. You have been through a lot in your life, tell me a couple hard things you faced and how you were able to handle the situation as well as you did.

4. Name one thing that each of the following people find impressive about you: Your teacher? Your grandmother? Your best friend?

5. What are the most positive changes you have made over the last year? Let's see if you can come up with at least five.

6. Today while we talk I am going to share with you the many positive improvements that you have made while we have been working together.

7. I am going to tell you today about some children who were hurt by their parents, and I will ask you in each case who was responsible for what happened.

8. As we work together to find the new Candace, I will hold up this paper stop sign each time the old Candace says

something in our session today, and we will let the new Candace say it instead.

9. You just said that Justin does not like you because you are not cool, tell me some other reasons that Justin acts toward you the way he does and I will help you think about it.

10. Tell me at least ten things you like about your body. Very good, now tell me ten things you like about your personality. Now I will tell you what I like about you.

2. Enhance neuro-integration

Executive functions of the frontal lobes of the neocortex require integration of functions in all parts of the brain. Neuro-integration is the brain's ability to access component parts to be integrated into an understandable whole that promotes good decision-making. Chapter 2 covered integration of the complex functions of the brain. Here it becomes goal number two due to how important it is for optimal mental health.

Unlike the first goal that is very straightforward, coming up with interventions to promote neuro-integration can be complex and initially confusing. The objective in the next few pages is to simplify a very complex issue. It is much easier to state the importance of the brain's various regions working together than it is to know how to help someone improve in this area.

There are many regions of the brain that play critical roles in optimal mental health. The often repeated statement we use only a small portion of our brain is not true. We rely on every part of our brain in daily life, but it makes a huge difference in efficiency and productivity if brain regions communicate and collaborate with each other. Some neuronetworks are more 'hard-wired' than others. An example is the brain regions that work together to provide the sense of sight through genetically built-in collaboration. If this were not true, the individual would be blind even if there were no structural problems. But the eyes work with the optic nerve sending what we experience as images to the occipital lobe where a part of the brain known as area 17 sends sensory information to the prefrontal cortex. The sensory input is then processed and understood to be an image. It is more complex than this outline of the process, but if any region of the brain fails to communicate in this chain of information sharing then the individual will not have functional sight. Most of us do not need outside interventions to be able to see and understand the meaning of what we see because the visual system is relatively hard-wired to function well.

Other regions of the brain are less genetically predisposed to work with the efficiency of our sense of sight. For example, it is easier to take advantage of sight than to learn to read. Reading requires many regions of the brain, including for most people the sense of sight itself. Reading is not hard-wired and for many people years of effort result in the frustration of being either a poor or even a non-reader. In general, the more complex the brain function, the more challenging it is to accomplish. Some of the most important brain functions that are highly valued by social networks are commonly known in sociology as social norms and mores. For example, as people we understand our competitive drives but we have social mores that do not value competition on the freeway, particularly if it results in a phenomena called 'road rage.' Socially we expect a mature driver to not retaliate when another driver makes a mistake or intentionally acts erratically. However, this higher order function is missing in a concerning number of drivers, a fact all too often observed on our roadways in America.

Some of the most important functions of the brain actually must curb our natural drives or what may be referred to as our baser and primitive instincts. We value mothers who put a child's needs above her own. We praise a father who would risk his life to protect his child from danger. We value soldiers who confront the most basic drive for survival by going into battle with bravery and courage. We are appalled at chief executive officers who take millions of dollars in bonuses as the company's financial stability crumbles. We expect mature teens and adults to modify their own needs for the needs of others and we call this empathy. Each of these societal values actually go against what we would do naturally and, therefore, these decisions must be specifically learned. The more complex the function of the brain, and the above examples are highly complex, the more the brain is required to collaborate among brain regions and to have an overriding decision-making component of the brain—the orbitofrontal cortex.

A component of neuro-integration is known by another term—sensory integration. However, neuro-integration includes the sensory systems but goes beyond them to include all brain regions working in unison. Neuro-integration is not a black or white proposition, as in you have it or you don't. It is more of a continuum of excellent, good, fair or poor. Because of these gradients, we all work to enhance neuro-integration throughout our lives. For example, we attempt to remember something important by combining, for example, the name of a good restaurant with eating there on a specific wedding anniversary. The brain may go directly to the name of the restaurant or start with the anniversary and end up with the restaurant name. This is a simple form of integrating neural information. More complex tasks such as walking only seem difficult when a person is either learning to do so at a young age or relearning to walk in older years after a stroke or traumatic brain injury. We never cease to more fully utilize our brain through enhancing the integration of brain functions. Most of the time this term is used there is a glaring weakness in the individual that may require intervention, but it is important to remember that no one has realized full neuro-integration.

If it is easier to point out the importance of neuro-integration and much more difficult to actually do it, then how is neuro-integration enhanced? The quick answer is any activity that engages multiple regions of the brain at the same time gives the brain practice at coordinating functions and communication between brain regions. However since the brain often uses multiple regions, to enhance neuro-integration it will help to 'stretch' the brain in ways it does not usually operate. For example, the brain of a traumatized child often uses sensory input processed by the limbic region of the brain, activating the autonomic nervous system and stress response cycle. In this example there are multiple brain regions involved, but the neuronetworks for this specific situation are well established and in fact are habituated due to constant use. Improving neuro-integration requires other brain regions to be exercised and learn to collaborate and process new sensory input rather than the default limbic/stress response. In order to do this, interventions need to help the brain operate differently and not process information in a status quo fashion.

The best way to enhance neuro-integration with children is to help them practice increasingly complex tasks with direction and support. External assistance is critical because the brain wants to be efficient and process information in the most familiar way.

A child who has a habit of processing mental information in a particular way will not change without outside assistance. The support is important because children tend to give up quickly when a mental task becomes difficult. Examples of complex tasks for children could be the mental activity of reading. Schools often encourage parents to read often with their children. This is a very good idea for many reasons, one of them being the impact on brain regions learning to work together in a new and more advanced way. With the example of reading, a parent should not pick the book that the child can easily read each time (although this may be the child's choice) because the brain will not be encouraged to increase the complexity of the mental process. When complexity is increased the neuropathways are changed and enhanced and through repetition the brain will change over time. Reading is a familiar mental task but there are other examples that will be suggested here as well.

There has been considerable focus in recent years over the budget cuts in schools that have affected 'extracurricular' activities such as physical education, team sports, music, drama and the arts. The proponents of making budget cuts in these areas say that the school can't do everything on ever tightening budgets and the 'core curriculum' must be maintained. The opponents of these cuts argue a healthy, well-educated individual needs a strong healthy body enhanced by physical exercise and education in the arts, which are skills just as important as the 'three R's.' From a brain perspective, the second argument would be the preferred position, the reason being enhanced neuro-integration.

Physical activity for a young person is an extremely complex combination of physical and mental tasks. In an overweight culture we often focus on burning off extra calories, but even more important is the body's ability to enhance the neuromaps leading to coordination and the body/brain functions allowing the individual to perform complex movements required of exercises and sports. An example of this is to watch a child jumping rope for the first time. The child attempts to use sight, proprioception (special awareness), hand/eye coordination and timing to attempt to accomplish this very difficult activity. However, with some practice the child can perform this feat while carrying on a conversation with a friend as if the brain was free to carry on other functions. The ability to jump rope is on the lower end of the complexity continuum when considering riding a bicycle, learning to dribble and shoot a basketball with another player trying to prevent you from doing so, or hitting a ball with a bat as it comes speeding toward you. Our society values excellence in sporting skills and abilities and encourages a child to become very proficient in a particular activity, such as a young Tiger Woods in golf or a Michael Phelps in swimming. However, once again from a brain perspective, we should value even more highly a well-rounded athlete who can perform a variety of complex mental/physical activities because the brain enhances its ability to coordinate cortical regions with each newly acquired skill.

Physical activity is an excellent method to enhance neuro-integration in children. Children generally like to be active and doing something new will often hold interest for them. However, once a child fails at a task (such as jumping rope) he or she may be less motivated to attempt a second time. A new activity requires many failures before becoming proficient. For this reason the child needs encouragement and support, particularly a child with a history of trauma who often has low personal confidence. Physical activities provide advantages beyond mental gains that make them a clear choice for children, such as social skills, endurance, coordination, childhood play, and the advantages to the body's immune system.

Creative expression of all types also encourages the brain regions to collaborate to perform complex tasks. Activities such as learning to play a musical instrument or even listening to music can enhance neuro-integration. Playing the piano, among other instruments, combines hand/eye coordination. Reading music, combined with hand and feet actions timed to produce a specific outcome are very complex brain processes involving multiple brain regions. In a similar way creative expression with crafts, painting, pottery, woodworking and many other activities help the brain to learn the essential ingredients of neuro-integration.

For professionals looking for specific activities as part of a mental health treatment intervention, a method to enhance neuro-integration is working with inter-hemispheric communication. The left and right hemispheres in the neocortex have somewhat different functions and in many ways operate as two distinct brains. Bringing the two brains into a collaborative team is what neuro-integration strives for. There are methods to promote or exercise the collaboration of the brain hemispheres, and every activity that does so promotes neuro-integration.

One activity that takes advantage of the functions of the left hemisphere (logical, analytic, verbal) and the right hemisphere (intuitive, artistic, emotive) is to have a child draw a picture using color and shapes that come from the child's imagination (right) and to have the child tell a story (left) associated with the picture. The same can be done with having a child close her eyes and listen to music and describe either emotions or images occurring in the brain from listening to the sounds. Every activity that requires the two hemispheres to work in unison, thus strengthening the corpus callosum , enhances neuro-integration. Repeated practice will be a vital component of enhancing collaboration.

It is not just children with traumatic backgrounds who need help in more fully developing neuro-integration. All children and all individuals need to practice making the brain more efficient and better coordinated. A general principle in this regard is that higher order brain skills do not necessarily develop on their own. It often takes systematic instruction. We make the mistake in our society to believe human beings learn complex mental operations naturally as they mature. For example, we expect young people to begin to show more and more empathy as they age, however, empathy does not come naturally to the brain when the needs of the other may supercede personal needs. We are surprised at the number of teens and adults in our society who seriously break our rules and land in our jails and prisons due to a variety of deficient mental functions such as delaying gratification, egocentricity, and lacking either social mores or a developed moral framework. These are some of the most complex higher order brain functions and do not come naturally. Another area of our society's collective discomfort is sexuality. Somehow we expect children with minimal mechanical information in our health classes to understand and function in a healthy way with the complexity of the social, physical, emotional and spiritual aspects of being a sexual person (Hindman, 2006). Living is complicated and healthy living can be extremely complicated. The more complex the mental functions requiring collaboration of brain regions (neuro-integration), the more instruction, practice, and support is needed to promote healthy development among young people. Neuro-integration is one of the most essential aspects of optimal mental health.

Here are some ways that neuro-integration can be improved:

1. Close your eyes and tell me first what you hear, now what your body feels sitting in the chair, now what you are thinking, now open your eyes and tell me all the colors you can see from where you are.

2. How calm is your body right now? Give me a number between 1 and 10, with 10 being very calm.

3. I have a fun puzzle for you to put together today; tell me when you think you know what the puzzle picture is.

4. Listen to this music and let your mind take you somewhere; now tell me where you went.

5. As I show you these pictures, tell me any feelings that come up inside of you.

6. Today we will be drawing a couple of pictures and I want you to tell me a story about the picture you drew.

7. I know you like to play "Simon Says," so let's play.

8. I will now read you a story and ask you some questions about what is going on with Jennifer in the story.

9. We will have a contest in our session today, I want to see if you can spot five feelings you are having then raise your hand and tell me what it is. If you get five you earn a prize.

10. Each week we will be covering a new superpower that your brain has; this week it will be empathy, or feeling what others are feeling.

3. Alter the region of the brain that processes information

The brain takes in thousands of sensory inputs every minute. Most of this information is background 'noise' and does not require nor deserve particular attention. For example, at any one time our auditory input includes sensory waves from people, from nature, from our own body and from the hum of civilization all around us. In fact, when you find yourself in a very quiet place, you may be surprised to learn silence can be quite loud due to giving more attention to the background noise all around. When an ambulance speeds by with the siren on, unless we are in the road there is no need to give this sensory input any significant attention. Much less obvious is the sound of the heating and cooling system coming on in an office building or people talking down the hall. The brain is trained to consider which sounds are important and which are not. The functional nature of making the decision as to importance is the brain's priority or processing system.

There are a number of areas of the brain that decide the prioritization of sensory input, chief among these areas are the limbic region and the prefrontal region. Both of these regions may be prioritizing different inputs and may be doing so simultaneously. When two brain regions conflict, past experience often determines which area has precedence.

The limbic region of the brain is a more advanced and complex area compared to the less complex brain stem and diencephalon, if any region of the brain can be called less complex. However, from an evolutionary perspective the majority of functions in the limbic region are more primitive than the prefrontal cortex, which is the most advanced and most newly developed region of the human brain. The evolution of the limbic region predates the evolutionary development of executive functions and processes important but somewhat primitive functions related to emotions, sexuality, sleep and wake cycles, and traumatic memory. Each of these functions has an overarching theme of promoting survival, the most critical of which is traumatic memories. The limbic region includes a number of structures including the hippocampus and amygdala. The first has a primary role in memory and the second has a primary role in responding to memory, but both focus primarily on survival.

The hippocampus does not get involved in external memory, such as recalling the address of the house we lived in when we turned sixteen. The hippocampus has a very specific job in remembering every negative experience that in any way threatened the person over the years. This includes and, in fact, prioritizes experiences before we had the ability to speak and communicate our experience with others. In this way the hippocampus was an advancement over the more primitive regions of the brain by connecting threats in the past (traumatic memories) with evasive action in the present (decision-making). The counterpart to the hippocampus is the amygdala which takes the lead role in responding to traumatic memories. The job of the amygdala is to sound the alarm based upon recalling the past and to initiate the stress response cycle resulting in the fight or flight response, or self-preservation response.

Traumatic events are stored with care in the brain because all life threatening experiences are best avoided if the goal is survival. However, there are multiple complexities related to traumatic memories that insure their primacy but limit their accuracy. For example, the recall of trauma is so critical that the focus is on reaction rather than a careful analysis, such as what actually happened in the past and what is actually happening in the present. The job of the limbic region is to react first and ask questions later. With this rapid response pattern to stimuli even generally associated with past traumatic events, the hippocampus signals the release of corticotropin release factor that in turn stimulates the pituitary and adrenal glands to produce adrenaline, norepinephrine and cortisol. The body then shuts down non-emergency systems and enables the flight/fight response. However, the release of these hormones impacts the ability of the hippocampus to supply the brain with details of the past event, such as how long ago an event may have taken place. For this reason there is a loss of time when it comes to trauma, the threatening experience either just happened or is ongoing because of this loss of a time frame. The result is a sensory processing system that is rapid and has excellent signal strength, but short on details of past events other than the basic equation of something bad has happened and is about to happen again, therefore, prepare to defend yourself.

Due to the lack of detail with traumatic memory, there is a significant chance negative associations will be generalized. For example, if a child nearly drowned in a swimming pool, he or she may avoid all water, including taking a bath. If a child was abused by a Latino step-dad, then all Latino males and, to be safe, all males should be avoided. The long-term impact of traumatic experience can be directly understood based upon this type of generalization of experience, which is a description of posttraumatic stress. The negative impacts of a sensory processing system centered in the limbic region include chronic stress due to over-activation of the stress response cycle, impaired self-regulation and other executive functions due to an undeveloped prefrontal cortex. These negative impacts in turn produce a host of other problems, including: sleep disturbances, hypervigilance, chronic reactivity, emotional dysregulation and associated issues such as learning problems. Another outcome of traumatic stress can be undeveloped executive functions including deficiencies in: planning, delaying gratification, thoughtful consideration and thinking before acting, ignoring distractions, sticking to a difficult task, logical thinking, using time management skills, learning from the past, initiating planful action, doing more than one thing at a time, self-awareness, self-regulation, inhibition of reactions, and many other important higher order mental functions.

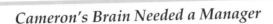

Cameron's Brain Needed a Manager

Nine-year-old Cameron came from a rural area where his family lived, isolated and distrusting outsiders. He was referred for intensive treatment because he was doing very poorly in school and even worse at home. It was fair to say that authorities also wanted him to be away from his unusual family to assess his needs. Cameron was either distant, silly, or aggressive and at times he switched these odd emotional states rapidly. His poor school performance and frequent vacant look had some professionals assuming he had low intelligence. However, when a full battery of testing was completed Cameron was above average. We began treating his overall issues as a problem with neuro-integration where his brain regions did not work together, leaving him confused and exhibiting his stress in silly or violent behavior. His treatment included building inter-hemispheric cohesion, development of his executive functions, emotional congruity, and building the decision-making part of his frontal lobes. Cameron had the necessary pieces but he needed his brain to put them together. As his brain worked more in harmony, his behaviors improved and his emotions began to fit the situation. His school performance improved and he began getting along with peers for the first time. Cameron now had a chance to use the mental tools he had all along.

In contrast to the limbic region, the prefrontal cortex has a similar priority on survival but goes about it very differently. Sensory input comes into the prefrontal region of the brain and is acted upon by the orbitofrontal cortex that processes a much wider range of input from multiple brain regions. Neural pathways run from the orbitofrontal cortex to the brain stem, the diencephalon, the limbic region and both right and left hemispheres in order to put the mental puzzles pieces together to create an intelligible picture. Only after the prefrontal region determines what is happening does it decide on a response. A fundamental difference exists in the sensory processing system of the limbic compared to the prefrontal cortex, and this difference is the amount of attention given to details. The limbic region responds immediately to threat and perceived threat and the goal is to live another day. The prefrontal region strives to understand the situation it is in and craft an effective response, therefore learning from the experience.

It is clear the optimal sensory processing region is the prefrontal cortex. It is not surprising the vast majority of individuals with significant histories of trauma have a predominant processing system based in the limbic region. A major part of treatment is to help the individual switch to a prefrontal dominated processing system. As with other aspects of treatment interventions, changing the processing system through which the individual understands and responds to the world is easier said than done.

A primary goal of all psychotherapy is to promote functioning of the higher reasoning centers of the brain. Enhancing the reasoning centers moves the individual away from reacting with fear and emotionality to reminders of previous negative experiences. The more functional alternative is for the higher reasoning centers of the neocortex to access information from all aspects of the brain and process the information to inform decisions and choices. Such a change may not be possible without expert therapeutic assistance.

Therefore, the overall plan for improving how the brain takes in and processes information and sensory input is to encourage the higher order reasoning center of the brain to play the predominant role. The first challenge for individuals with traumatic histories is to address the way the brain will nearly always process information, and that will be through the limbic region. The only effective way to change this is to build the prefrontal cortex to become stronger and more internally influential than the reactive and instantaneous limbic response. One of the best ways to accomplish this is through relaxation.

Relaxation is the process of reducing the amount of perceived stress. The best forms of relaxation combine mind/body approaches such as breathing, focused movement such as Yoga and Tai Chi, and autogenics (a combination of body posture, visualization and decompressing stress). The body will in most cases take its lead from the brain and the prefrontal cortex has the ability, when this skill is developed, to refocus the processing of input into the brain.

Relaxation turns off the stress response cycle and therefore prevents unnecessary exposure to the release of cortisol. Relaxation also strengthens the resiliency of the individual by enhancing the ability of the person to cope with initially stressful situations and events. Relaxation also calms the autonomic nervous system and stimulates the parasympathetic nervous system to reduce stress. Relaxation also promotes better sleeping patterns which assists in the consolidation of memories, further promoting mental health.

Relaxation does so many good things that it is a mental health treatment in and of itself.

Stated briefly, any activity that requires the brain to use the higher reasoning center of the prefrontal cortex will help retrain the information processing system. The tried and true intervention to ask a child to 'use your words' is a good way to encourage the speech center of the neocortex (Broca's Area) to process information coming from sensory information and from the emotional center (limbic region) as well. Encourage a child to consider choices and ask them to describe what they are thinking or feeling. The one intervention most often used by adults is not recommended, which is asking a child 'why' they acted the way they did. Adults generally get a very honest reply to the 'why' question and that is, 'I don't know.'

Another helpful intervention is to help a child practice the 'three R's' which in this case are: Relax, Rethink and Respond. Relaxation has been addressed. Rethinking encourages the child to bring consideration to the situation. Only with the foundation of the first two R's can the child learn to move beyond reacting to responding, indicating a thoughtful reply to a situation. Yet another way to achieve this goal is to teach a child when frustrated to go through a process such as stop, take a deep breath, and make a request.

The way to change the most often used processing system of the brain requires the individual to think first, feel second and act third and not the reverse order. The reactive limbic region of the brain cannot be the primary part of the brain used. The person must learn to act rather than react in all areas of living.

Here are some examples of ways to help change the part of the brain that processes sensory input:

1. I want to start and stop our therapy session today with both of us practicing our relaxation steps: 1—close our eyes, 2—take a deep breath, and 3—say out loud to ourselves, "I can handle this." Now I want to talk about how upset you were at school today, tell me what you were thinking when you got upset.

2. You look very upset right now. I want you to clench your fists as tight as you can and slowly relax them. Now tell me what you are thinking, what you are feeling, and what can you do to make things better.

3. I am going to read to you several situations and in each one tell me the best decision the young person can make.

4. Right now there is a lot going on inside you, slow down and tell me what you are feeling.

5. I know you are frightened of spiders, so after you practice your three steps to relax I want you to look at these pictures of spiders while you stay calm.

6. Before we talk about your feelings about your Dad, let's both sit in our calm position for a couple minutes.

7. You look a little tense, what is your body saying to you right now?

8. You got very upset at recess just now, let's you and I take a short walk and calm down together.

9. You react when James teases you, I will try to tease you and you practice being stronger than I am and not letting me upset you.

10. Today in our session we are going to get excited and then get calm several times, it will be fun — let's start.

4. Facilitate orbitofrontal cortex activation

The optimal goal of brain processing is to activate the orbitofrontal cortex in the prefrontal lobes of the neocortex. It is in this most complex part of the brain where information from all other parts of the brain is subject to deliberation and proactive mental activity. This is the opposite of the reactivity of much of the limbic brain region. This prefrontal cortex region of the brain can be viewed as the chief executive officer because it is not only the most complex region, it has the potential of being the most productive region due to executive functions such as: cause and effect reasoning, goal setting, planning, strategic thinking, moral and ethical reasoning, accurate interpretations, understanding communication, using past experiences to promote current and future success, organized logical thinking, self-evaluation, insight, assimilating new information, goal-directed actions, overriding emotional reactivity, delaying gratification, self-regulation, mental flexibility, sustained mental effort, filtering distractions, focusing attention, complex thinking and expressions, determining appropriate social responses, problem-solving and adjusting behavior based upon feedback.

This long list of higher order reasoning enables the brain to take advantage of its remarkable potential. Without these mental tools the brain's potential goes unrealized. The difference between this region being optimized or unrealized is whether the neurotemplates of the orbitofrontal cortex are not only developed but are frequently used and strengthened. Perhaps the best way to show the importance of this region of the prefrontal cortex is to show what happens when damage occurs to this part of the brain.

Chapter 1 mentioned the story of Phineas Gage. But we do not have to go back more than a century to illustrate what damage to this part of the brain does. Individuals with traumatic brain injury often have similar stories like the following case of a career officer in the Air Force.

The family called in for help with a child's acting-out behavior. In the first session it was clear the seven-year-old boy was saying with his behaviors he was unable to cope with family pressures that every member was feeling, each in their own way. Sometimes the child acting-out may be the most functional member of the family in situations like this. The family was changed in an instant when the father, a Colonel and pilot in the Air Force, had a glider accident where his head hit the windshield during a landing in wind shear conditions. He recovered from the serious concussion, or did he? When the family came in for help, the accident had occurred eight months earlier. The patience of the family, particularly his wife, to his healing process was wearing thin. This intelligent, gentle, supportive husband and father, was transformed by the injury into a sullen, angry, explosive tyrant around the house. All the family wanted was to have the man they knew returned to them rather than this stranger who no longer fit in, something no one could give them.

Much like poor Phineas Gage, the above story reflects the critical importance of the prefrontal cortex, exactly what is damaged in head trauma due to collisions with windshields. Many of the executive functions become strong components of the identity of the person or what we consider the personality. How a person thinks, feels and acts, what he or she believes, how they treat others and what they are like to be around are all important components of who a person is. Physical and even psychological trauma to the prefrontal cortex can change all of these characteristics of a person and much more.

Activating the orbitofrontal cortex as a part of the treatment process is the reverse of traumatic brain injury. We start with a state of disrepair and develop a more functional decision-making component of the brain. Reading the long list of higher order functions mentioned above, and this is not a complete list by any means, shows the critically important role this small part of the brain must play. Without it the brain has unrealized potential or is chaotically dysfunctional.

The goal over time is to have the individual process most information in the most advanced area of the neocortex. For individuals with traumatic histories, only this region of the brain has the ability to override the limbic region for dominance. Promoting higher order reasoning is not only the goal of Neurological Reparative Therapy, it is also a fundamental aspect of becoming a mature functioning person. However, traumatized individuals often have impediments that must be worked with to make room for the development of the orbitofrontal cortex. Interventions promoting the development of this region of the brain include familiar teaching and learning tools used for all children, teens and adults.

In a sentence, every intervention that promotes thoughtful consideration exercises the orbitofrontal cortex. This covers a great many techniques and approaches. One of the best is what every good parent does with a developing child — talk to them and help them think about a situation and consider a good response. To a real extent this process provides stimulation of the orbitofrontal cortex from outside the brain. In other words, the parent's brain is helping the child's brain think in more complex ways. Whether the neural firing is internally or externally initiated, the firing will strengthen the development of this part of the prefrontal cortex.

Adults naturally take children aside and help them consider a situation and ask them to look at options. This is the basis of coaching, teaching in school, mentoring and, of course, good parenting. To this list we need to add therapists. The therapist is in a particularly strong position to help a child develop higher order reasoning because of lack of a need to be the source of rules and requirements. Therapists have an access to children that few others have and this can be utilized to help the child improve thoughtful consideration and reasoning.

There is no universally agreed upon system to categorize the human brain and some scientists include the limbic region or parts of it in the prefrontal cortex. The orbitofrontal cortex connects directly with the limbic region and in this book a distinction is made between these two regions of the brain. For the orbitofrontal cortex to be dominant over the limbic region, it must win the tug-of-war for which input wins — reactive survival-based fight or flight on the one hand or thoughtful consideration based upon learning from past experience on the other. One way to facilitate thoughtful consideration is to increase the ability of the individual to have internal self-awareness (yet another executive function). By increasing awareness the person can anticipate limbic stress and be prepared to modify it. The nature of limbic reactivity initiates the nervous system instantly, a critical component of surviving when a speeding car is headed towards you. However, awareness can modify the limbic stress before it has the chance to create a full response in the pituitary and adrenal glands activating the whole body. For example, testing the fire alarm in school is often prefaced by an announcement of a drill, otherwise the limbic region's amygdala reacts in hundreds of children simultaneously. If the child knows the fire alarm will soon sound or for that matter is familiar with the meaning of the loud irritating noise, then the orbitofrontal cortex brings meaning to the auditory sensory input and the child can either ignore the sound or calmly stand up and file out of the building. If a loud explosion were to go off in an elementary school, the result would likely be very different than an orderly response to a drill.

There is a positive synergy to the development of the orbitofrontal cortex, the more executive functions are exercised the more deliberation and reasoning occurs. Small improvements can lead to greater improvements in a geometrical trend line. The following are a number of specific methods of enhancing the orbitofrontal cortex or decision-maker of the brain:

1. Have the child put together ever increasingly difficult puzzles, helping him or her to integrate pieces to see the overall picture.

2. Give a child a problem and several choices for a response and have him pick a solution and explain why.

3. Teach a child how to breakdown a problem into component parts and consider a solution based upon such analysis.

4. In developmentally appropriate ways, explain the fundamentals of logic and how this leads to insight.

5. Teach a child the benefits of delaying gratification.

6. Help a child learn to save money to reach a goal of a major purchase such as a bike, thus teaching goal-setting and goal-directed behavior.

7. Help a child see the relationship of cause and effect and how to think about the results of actions (this is best done when the child is not in trouble).

8. Before the individual makes the same habitual mistake, remind her what happened the last time and see if a new plan could be considered with a better outcome.

9. Give a child a number of social situations and ask what is going on and what the situation calls for. For example, you have dinner at Grandma's and she forgot you do not like liver and onions, what should you do when you find out what she plans for dinner?

10. Help a child grow in mental flexibility by having her identify several ways she could handle a common situation and then try a new approach never tried before.

5. Neurotemplate development through repetitive practice

By far the easiest goal to explain in this chapter is how neurotemplates develop—practice, practice and more practice. Networks of communication in the brain are made possible by neurotemplates and their individual component parts—neurons. Neurons have a use dependent developmental process where neurons that are frequently used become larger and stronger as well as do work faster. In contrast, neurons that are never used may atrophy and die (known as apoptosis), and if neurons are seldom used they can gradually deteriorate. One key goal of exercising the brain is repetition, since it is in repeated use that neurons and neurotemplates, composed of millions of individual neurons, get more frequent use. The more use, the stronger and more capable the brain functioning becomes.

Repetition aids the process of neurotemplate development in several ways. The first has been mentioned in that neurons must do work by firing electrically and initiating chemical transfers to other neurons in order to stay alive. Another way that repetition aids development is how the electrical activity through the axon of the neuron promotes the development of layers of protein called myelin. The more myelin that coats the axon, the more efficiently the electrical charge travels to the dendrites. Efficiency in this case includes the speed and strength of the electrical signal. The speed of the electrical signal in a healthy axon is approximately 250 miles per hour. It takes this very rapid pace to allow the body to perform complex functions such as run after a soccer ball and change directions quickly. For such a complex motor activity to take place, many millions of neurons must send electrical and chemical messages almost instantly. A very small decrease in the speed or signal of the electrical charge due to damaged or inadequate myelin can produce profound negative consequences in the functioning of the body.

Another way repetition helps is in the development and strengthening of the dendrites making chemical contact with other neurons. Every new brain activity results in new connections within the brain, and the more this activity is repeated the stronger the connections become. This is the mechanical aspect of how the brain changes with all brain responses to the environment.

The process of repetition has one major challenge—the wrong type of repetition strengthens negative coping and poor response patterns. After traumatic experiences the individual can become stuck in habitual patterns of reactivity. Each habitual thought or action becomes stronger and stronger with repetition and can be very difficult to change. This is one of many reasons why trauma treatment is better early on rather than later on, and why the right type of treatment provided to young children has more impact than the same treatment later in life.

Therefore, repetitive practice facilitates this goal. The expression 'practice makes perfect' refers to the importance of repetitive efforts to improve the results. The brain changes gradually over time through the repetitive use of families of neurons that help us to do daily tasks such as play the piano, type on the computer, or hear critical feedback without reacting with anger. The more practice the brain has, the more the brain changes.

Here are some interventions that can help reach this goal:

1. Let me show you how to tie your shoe, now you try it. That was a very good try, let's do it again.

2. You are becoming a good reader, read that last paragraph for me again.

3. Write your address on the paper and I will time you to see how many times you can write it in three minutes, go!

4. For therapists, start and end a session by having the child practice a skill that fits his or her treatment.

5. For teachers, you have all your spelling words correct except 'detour,' after you write the word ten times I will give you a chance to spell it again and get a 100%.

6. I know you feel bad about hitting your brother, so you can play with him again if you can tell me three better ways to handle it when he cheats at cards.

7. I will let you make the cookies you want if you can tell me three times correctly what the ingredients are and the five steps to make them.

8. For a coach, you want to make your free throws next time so I want you to make 50 shots each day before the big game on Saturday.

9. For adults, you can lower your golf score if you make your putts so start at four feet and when you can make five in a row, move to five feet and repeat.

10. For anyone trying anything, do that again because every time you do it you get a little bit better at it.

The principle of the brain's ability to make positive change can no longer be considered a theory; it is a fact. Promoting positive brain change can no longer be considered too complex to understand; it can be explained in a straightforward manner. Coming up with interventions to help the brain positively is a daily challenge, but it is necessary. While the ability of the brain to make positive changes is encouraging, there is an element of sadness that comes with the optimism. The great potential of the human brain will often not be realized in many children, not because it is beyond our understanding or capacity, but because adults in the child's life will not put in the required effort. The next two chapters will outline procedural steps in promoting brain adaptation. It will require supportive adults with a long-term commitment to make potential become a reality.

The Five Goals of NRT

Goal 1—Change the way the person perceives self, others and the environment.

Goal 2—Enhance neuro-integration or how the brain internally communicates.

Goal 3—Alter the part of the brain that processes information.

Goal 4—Activate the decision maker of the brain the orbitofrontal cortex.

Goal 5—Make lasting changes in the brain through repetitive practice.

Chapter

5

The Five Procedural Steps of Neurological Reparative Therapy

Establishing goals is only part of the process, there must also be a strategy or process to accomplish the goal. Achieving the goal of brain change requires at least a basic understanding of how the brain operates. In addition to consideration of the brain regions, electrical and chemical processes, and how neurotransformation takes place, the brain also has what could be called fascinating personality characteristics. For example:

- The brain dislikes tedium, which helps explain why we daydream and how our minds wander.

- The brain is essentially competitive with internal neural networks competing for attention and dominance.

- The brain likes to learn and change.

- The brain pursues rewards and pleasurable sensations.

- The brain becomes restless when it does not get the stimulation and activity it enjoys.

- Even when the body sleeps the brain is very much awake and active.

- The brain is always learning new ways to learn.

Rough comparisons of the human brain to a computer fail to take into account the fact that the brain is a living, changing organism. It cannot be turned off, it changes and heals itself, and it has interests and motivations as well as internal reward systems. Each of the above characteristics of the human brain can assist in promoting desired neurotransformation.

The Five Steps of NRT

Following the five goals in the last chapter, five more ingredients make up the ten principals of Neurological Reparative Therapy. In this chapter the practical application of NRT will be expanded by outlining the five procedural steps of the process of treatment. This chapter will answer the question, "How do I go about this process and in what order?" Unlike the goals in Chapter 4, the five steps toward neurological repair outlined below are sequential and provide a process where each step builds upon the previous step. It is important each step occur in the proper order to enable the process to build in an optimal healing fashion.

To a degree the five steps involved in this process follow a standard assessment model, but with some adjustments. For example, the process of psychological treatment must always begin with a good assessment of the nature and extent of the problem or concern and this is where we begin with step one.

1. Assess the extent and causes of neurological impairment

All information available should be used to determine the extent of neurological impairment as well as the primary causes of the impairment. Traumatic events are the most common causes of serious neurological impairment. Most problem areas have identifiable symptoms that point to both the level of intensity and the causal factors. A good evaluation and history will normally provide sufficient information. A variety of psychological rather than medical instruments are available to assist in the assessment phase.

A new dynamic has developed in recent years. The general public has learned of the new technologies available to study and do research on the brain. In addition, advertisers constantly tell the public to "ask your doctor" about our medication. An outgrowth of the media information on sophisticated brain scans and the encouragement to ask for what you want has led to requests by parents for brain scans of their children. If families insist on a treatment protocol that includes brain scans for the child, it is possible to find this resource. However, the efficacy of using scans on individual children for treatment purposes is more than controversial, it is suspect at this point in the evolution of brain science. While there is no question about the value of various brain scans for research purposes for groups of individuals, the research is not conclusive that scans provide information that is not accessible in other less costly methods. The practical question is whether a brain scan is likely to alter the prescribed treatment of an individual child, and this is seldom answered in the affirmative. The general position in the field of using brain science in the therapeutic process is it is not essential to use complex medical scans to identify impairment, but it is possible this will change in the future.

Rather than starting the assessment process with a brain scan, start at the beginning with a good assessment of the individual's history and current functioning in all areas. While less exciting and scientifically compelling than a functional Magnetic Resonance Imaging (fMRI), a well-done traditional assessment will nonetheless get the job done. A variety of formats and approaches to a good assessment and NRT allow room to approach the assessment using multiple methods.

The more the treating professional knows about the history, the positive and negative influences on the individual, and how the person responds to a variety of challenges in life (particularly the response to various forms of stress), the better chance of starting treatment on a solid foundation.

A comprehensive assessment will include all the standard elements such as: family history, developmental history, prenatal care, any birth trauma, developmental milestones, parental history of drug or alcohol use, any criminal history, development of attachment, mental status, school and academic progress, problematic affect or behaviors and any symptoms of a mental health disorder.

In addition to these standard topics in a mental health assessment, it is helpful to go into some detail regarding the child's cognitive skills. Cognitive testing can be helpful to determine if there are intellectual deficiencies rather than a lack of neuro-integration, where the abilities are present but not integrated or working properly. Assessing for adaptive skills including socialization, communication and living skills helps identify areas of deficiency. Finally, it is helpful to go over a variety of executive functions and ask a parent or guardian to indicate the strengths and weaknesses in each of these areas. With the above information, you will have much more practical information than any brain scan can tell you.

It is always a good idea during the assessment phase to obtain information from more than one source. On a scale of attachment, it is frequently the case that the mother and the father rate the child differently in terms of the bond they experience. To some degree this should be the case because a child has different connections with different people. However, many times the difference in scores is a difference in perception. Assessment information is helpful from all direct care providers, teachers, previous therapists, a grandparent and perhaps a coach. Do not be surprised that after multiple inputs the child represents a more complex picture than the identified problem presented at intake.

Knowing about past events is only a starting place during the assessment because events do not traumatize a person, it is the impact of the events on the individual. How the individual processes and responds to the event, rather than the event itself, determines if the person is able to cope or becomes overwhelmed, thus traumatized. Some children face terrible situations and bounce back in surprisingly remarkable shape, while others are traumatized by relatively minor events. With information about the event, you can then find out how the child perceived the situation, or learn from guardians how the child responded to events in the past. Trauma is a highly individualized experience and it is essential to consider only the level of trauma the individual experienced, not what someone else or the average person would have experienced.

With a complete assessment the foundation is laid for a solid plan. As will be covered in more detail in the next chapter, unless you know the right problem, you are unlikely to be successful regardless of the quality or quantity of your interventions.

2. Identify specific cognitive, emotional and behavioral problematic impairments

Up to this point there is little that distinguishes a NRT assessment from any other quality mental health assessment. The differences in this model begin to be clear in Step 2. When the assessment is completed, the initial issues that need attention will begin to come to the surface. However, there are often obvious emotional and behavioral problems, but some of the brain impairment and the interactions of brain regions may take longer to become clear. Regardless of the area of impairment it is critical to accurately identify the right problem, rather than the most obvious problem, and consider the likely causes. Frequently with all forms of impairment, the representation of the problem area on the surface can look like an entirely different issue than the source of the impairment. Here is where the detective work in the field of psychology comes into play. The best clinicians are not the ones with the most advanced degrees or certification in the latest evidence-based practice, the best clinicians are like skilled car mechanics who notice the symptoms and can identify the right problem the first time. For example, one reason so many children are treated for ADHD is because the symptoms are nearly identical to the observable impacts of trauma on young children. It is easy to write a script for a stimulant, it is much more difficult and time consuming to develop a plan for addressing past trauma. In another example, most firesetters have problems other than pyromania (unhealthy fascination with fire) such as needing attention, expressing a cry for help or reflecting unresolved anger. In a real sense, Step 2 is the second aspect of a comprehensive assessment.

Behavioral issues are usually the most obvious to identify. In fact, most children (and adults) present for mental health treatment with a list of problems which are generally behaviors unwanted at home or at school. It can be a mistake for the therapist to take the presenting problem behaviors and begin to develop a plan to work on them. Typically, if the child is hyperactive medication is considered, if the child sexually acts out psychosocial treatment is considered, and if the child is aggressive and violent a structured plan to reduce the child's frustrations is implemented. In the context of this chapter, the above treatment directions constitute a rush to the intervention stage and this occurs far too frequently than it should in mental health clinics across the country.

In the field of psychology there have been a number of different approaches to understanding behaviors. In the early stages of psychology, behaviors were outgrows of subconscious drives. Next it was the behavior itself that became the dominant issue and all intervention was behaviorally focused. Both of these paradigms have for the most part fallen out of favor and more complex outgrowths of both are more widely accepted, such as genetic influences on behavior rather than the subconscious, or cognitive influences on behavior rather than stimulus/response behaviorism. It is time for psychology to take advantage of brain science and go to the next logical step to consider how the symptoms of the problem directly relate to the neurological factors that may, in many cases, be the direct cause of the problem. This is the precise focus of Neurological Reparative Therapy. How this view changes the focus of treatment comes next.

Emotional problems are often on the presenting problem list. Emotions play a critical role in many important developmental areas including: social and relational skills, internal regulation, self-understanding, resiliency, self-healing and attachment (Denham, 1998). Social success becomes more and more important as a child advances in age as do the skills of correctly interpreting the intentions of others, what other people are thinking, being aware of a wide range of emotions, and the ability to manage one's feelings (Eisenberg, Fabes, Gutherie & Reiser, 2000). Cognitions and emotions are closely linked and if emotions are impaired, thinking can also be impaired due to development of areas of the brain including: the prefrontal cortex, the limbic region, the hypothalamus and brainstem, among others (Davidson, Lewis, Alloy, Amaral, Bush, & Cohen, 2002).

Responding to emotional problems in children can be vulnerable to the same linear problem-solving approach as behavioral therapy: A + B = C, where A is the situation, B is the emotional outburst, leading to C the intervention. However, the human brain does not breakdown in the syllogistic framework of logic. There is a simplistic formula that is more often accurate than inaccurate where A stands for the neurological perceptions and processing of information of the individual, B stands for the resulting emotional response, and C stands for the externalized behavior that is observable. One exception to this formula is some of the emotionally-based issues involved in bipolar disorder, although it is frequently over-diagnosed. Using this revised formula, the best way to change behavioral and emotional problems is to work back upstream and get to the perceptions that are generally the cause of both.

Emotions follow perceptions because it is not an event that produces an emotional response, it is how the individual perceives the event. If a person is called into her supervisor's office and learns that her work performance has been greatly appreciated and she will receive a 7% pay raise, the affective response will likely be quite positive. However, after being in the lunch room and learning that a coworker who continually takes credit for the work of others was also called in and given a 10% pay raise, the positive affect will predictably go in a very different direction. A similar scenario could occur where hard times have resulted in an across-the-board pay cut of 20% for all employees, but a particularly valued employee is called in and told the cut will only be 10% due to exceptional work performance, the perceptions of the reduction will likely be based on relative issues of comparisons with the other employees. In fact, it would not be surprising that the same employee in the second scenario would feel better about the situation than the employee in the first example even though the pay difference would be significantly more negative. The point is that it is not external events that produce feelings, it is the person's perception and the internal meaning given to the events that matters most. For most emotionally-based problems, the perceptions of the person will need to be addressed.

One of the best ways to identify neurological issues was mentioned in Step 1, through consideration of executive functions and making a list of both strengths and weaknesses in these higher order reasoning skills. It is likely that a background of trauma (which includes the majority of clients who present for mental health treatment) will involve the challenges to effective stress management due to limbic reactivity. If the child's cognitive abilities are not impaired and yet the child seems unable to take advantage of the abilities he or she does have, then there may be a problem of efficient and collaborative neuro-integration among brain regions. With very few exceptions, problem behaviors and emotional problems will be neurologically based.

To summarize Step 2, insure that the initial assessment includes a careful focus on what the real issues are and what has caused them. Only when we know the right problem do we have a chance at finding the right solution.

3. Implement interventions addressing the identified problematic emotional and behavioral symptoms

Once it is clear what the causes of the neurological impairment are, the next step is to design interventions that address the emotional and behavioral symptoms in light of the causes identified in the previous step. Since behavior is an observable sign of the individual's perceptual beliefs, or inner working model, cognitions are the focus of treatment as well as emotional and behavioral interventions. There are many possible approaches that can be used for specific interventions, including a large number of evidence-based practices. While the approach used may cause the treatment to fail, by itself the approach will not be the reason for success. Research has consistently shown that who the therapist is and how he or she conducts the therapy is the primary ingredient of success. The NRT model would also stress not only the competence of the therapist but also the importance of identifying the right problem to address and then impacting the brain to make a lasting difference in the life of the client.

After the correct problem is identified in the first two steps, the process of developing interventions is so critical that the next chapter will be devoted to how to use the brain to move the child from problems to progress. For that reason a detailed account of developing effective interventions will not be provided here. However, as an overview, the important elements are to translate the meaning of the target symptom of the child, consider any issues in the person's past such as traumatic experiences, and only then begin to consider how to move the individual from where they are to where they need to go. As in any journey, it is essential to first know where your destination is and second to determine the means to get to the goal. With these two elements firmly established, the journey itself can be less stressful and even enjoyable.

The principle that the brain is changeable throughout life is only recently becoming common knowledge. However, there have been bold experiments and resulting theories that have been tested over the past four decades. The old belief that the brain develops early in life and gradually but inexorably solidifies and loses its ability to change has given way to an acceptance of brain adaptation (neurotransformation or plasticity) at all ages of life. While this is an incredibly positive statement about the brain and an extremely hopeful implication for brain repair, neuroscience has been slow in accepting this position. Over time it has become increasingly difficult to question continual brain adaptation based upon decades of studies like the following:

- The brain learned to "see" where there was only blindness before through stimulation of the visual cortex (Bach-y-Rita, Collins, Saunders, White & Scadden, 1969; Bach-y-Rita, 1972).

- The amount of education throughout life increases the connections among neurons (Jacobs, Schall & Scheibel, 1993).

- Autistic children improved attention span, sense of humor and reduced autistic symptoms (Melzer & Poglitch, 1998).

- Children with dyslexia were given an intervention and new brain scans showed their brains improved (Temple, Deutsch, Poldrack, Miller, Tallal, Merzenich & Gabrieli, 2003).

Regardless of the branch of science, ironically there are beliefs that persist beyond studies that show the contrary. In the case of neuroscience, the unchanging brain, the fixed nature of the brain following insults, and the permanency of brain damage are beliefs that have persisted contrary to mounting evidence to the contrary. The changing brain is no longer being considered an aberration or an unexplained finding, neuroscientists now expect to see adaptation and neurotransformation due to treatments designed to promote positive improvement. One way to define psychotherapeutic interventions are methods to change the structure of brain neurons as well as altering neural networks (Vaughan, 1997). Brain change goes deeper than a surface focus on emotional and behavioral improvement, but working with behaviors and emotions that we can see is the starting point of effective treatment.

Rosa Learned the Importance of Trust

Rosa was only ten years old by the time she came to Jasper Mountain Center. She was diagnosed with juvenile diabetes and used her eating and her insulin needles as ways to threaten others or manipulate her world. Her health was in serious jeopardy when she arrived for mental health treatment. In addition to health problems, at her early age she had already experienced years of childhood neglect, physical and verbal abuse, and severe sexual abuse by numerous caregivers. Her mother had sought out services for Rosa multiple times, and by this time she had had a long list of therapists and therapeutic interventions. Although she had received every type of intensive therapeutic service, nothing had been successful up to this point. She arrived at Jasper Mountain Center hopeless, angry, rageful, demanding, aggressive and refusing to cooperate or open up to anyone, especially her therapist. It took about seven months before Rosa would begin to trust and allow anyone to hear her story. Over time Rosa made many improvements in all areas. However, most importantly she learned the value of communicating her pain, discovering the lies she was told, speaking the truth, and giving herself permission to be happy and receive love. Rosa is now in a long-term family placement, is succeeding academically, and is healthy and active on her local track and field team. She has a long run ahead of her but she is now taking it on one lap at a time and feeling pretty good about her progress, and so am I.

Marta Prato, M.S.W.

As will be covered in the next chapter, behaviors are the most observable problem issues, but they arise from how the child thinks and feels about everything in the environment. The best way to make lasting change is to start with perceptions, then move to emotional responses and the combination of these two result in externalized behaviors. NRT does not specify a particular vehicle to use since the important element is the therapist using the approach they believe in, as well as having training and experience. However, while any particular approach is not identified by NRT, it does stress the important element of targeting the brain and therefore changing the person from the inside out.

4. Decondition the child's stress response cycle through multiple forms of relaxation and allostatic training

Stress can be either a positive or negative influence on the development of the individual, the difference is often the degree to which the individual can cope with the stress. The ability to cope has significant consequences for physical and mental health throughout life. Stress can be categorized into three areas: 1. Positive stress—moderate and manageable stress that helps the individual master stress, 2. Tolerable stress—brief negative stress with the presence of a support system producing coping, and 3. Toxic stress—strong, prolonged activation of the stress response cycle without a sufficient support system (Shonkoff, Boyce, Cameron, Duncan, Fox, Gunnar, Levitt, McEwen, Nelson, Phillips & Thompson, 2005). Toxic stress is a frequent outgrowth of early traumatic experiences and is often found in children who are presented for mental health services. Toxic stress often has an adverse impact on developing brain circuitry and can lead to poorly controlled stress responses and poor health and well-being (McEwen, 2008).

The most common problems associated with neurological impairment are the wide range of negative influences of neurological adaptations to traumatic experiences. There are many other impairments of a neurological nature, but adaptations to negative past experiences are by far the most frequent. The brain is always sensing ways it can adapt to promote the individual's interests. Unfortunately, not all adaptations are helpful or beneficial. It is also unfortunate traumatic experiences shut down the very brain systems needed to evaluate and understand what is and is not a positive adaptation. For example, a fundamental negative adaptation to trauma is hyperarousal and loss of self-regulation due to the stress response leading to a systemic fight/flight activation of the autonomic nervous system. Regions of the brain understand that these adaptations actually put up barriers to being successful. Located in the prefrontal cortex, these regions are relegated a much lower priority than the fight or flight response.

One of many challenges to helping the brain accurately assess the best response to situations after trauma is to reduce stress and elevate the status of the prefrontal region where self-awareness originates. The first task is therefore to identify ways the individual can reduce stress both acutely and chronically.

Research has identified many forms of relaxation are the most effective tools to decondition the overactivation of the stress response cycle. It turns out one of the most basic and simple tools is one of the best. Most parents spend great amounts of time starting soon after birth to help a child reduce stress through soothing touch and a reassuring voice. A more technical term for deconditioning stress is allostasis, or the process of the nervous system and the brain starting at baseline then going into stress mode and then being able to return to baseline once again. Most people are familiar with a companion term, homeostasis, which is the ability of the nervous system and the brain to stay very close to baseline or minimal arousal. While homeostasis is achievable and helpful for machines such as a room thermostat, the same cannot be said for people who go up and down in stress continually.

Allostatic training involves assisting the individual to return to a state of calm after arousal, which is the allostatic response. Stress is a constant in life and the ability to self-soothe and regain an inner state of calm is critical to handling the ever present stresses of life. The most important element of the allostatic process is the ability to come down from arousal or return to baseline or a state of calm. Most people do not need training to become aroused, but most people need help in learning how to reduce stress and the accompanying symptoms once stress is registered in the brain.

Stress is so pervasive and endemic to living that it is not a realistic goal to achieve a homeostatic state in life for more than brief periods. It is very helpful to understand and to practice and master the ability to calm down once the state of arousal has hit the brain, nervous system and stress hormones. There are huge gains for the individual to be able to return to a state of calm in the midst of chronic and/or situational stress. The ability to relax is so helpful and so important that it must be an aspect of most mental health therapy.

Although stress is a universal experience, how stress is managed is somewhat unique to the individual. Clearly some individuals cope with a great deal more stress than others. Both in a medical and mental health perspective, significant trauma in the past is often associated with significant difficulties dealing with moderate to mild stress. The mechanisms within the brain that respond to stress are similar and Figure 1 gives a snapshot of stress and the brain.

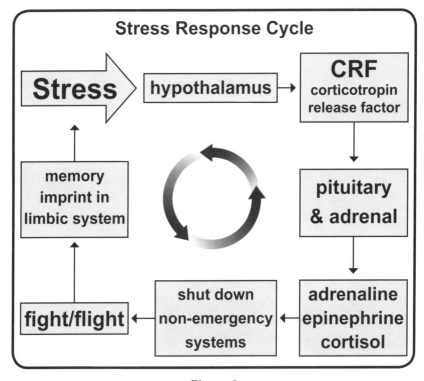

Figure 1

Stress is picked up by the brain through sensory experience combined with situations from the past that help the brain determine the level of stress as well as the response to the stress. When the brain senses any stress it considers important, the information is processed first by the hypothalamus which signals the release of corticotropin releasing factor or CRF in order to provide an adequate response to a potentially threatening stressor. CRFs indicate to the pituitary and adrenal glands that three hormones are to be released to travel throughout the body –

adrenaline, epinephrine and cortisol. Adrenaline is produced by the sympathetic-adrenomedullary system and cortisol by the hypothalamic-pituitary-adrenocortical system. These stress hormones can play an important positive role in the body's response to stress. However, in chronic or toxic stress the results can be adverse impacts on managing stress, impaired emotions and poor memory functioning (Sapolsky, Romero & Munch, 2000), and hinder learning and the healthy architecture of the brain (McEwen & Sapolsky, 1995). The corresponding impact on the body of these hormones is to shut down 'non-emergency' bodily systems while sending blood flow to major muscle groups in the body resulting in the ability to initiate a systemic response to the stress, often called the fight or flight response. In extreme and rare cases this is a needed response to, for example, move away from an approaching speeding vehicle. At such a time the needed action is immediate flight and not to consider the size and weight of the vehicle, the estimated speed and the potential skill of the driver. All these considerations are immediately overridden by the body moving out of the way.

While the fight/flight response is an important survival system, seldom are most individuals in a life threatening situation and therefore the fight/flight response is much too strong a response to a stress that is a very limited threat to survival. Because the process outlined above referred to as the stress response cycle is often unnecessary and insufficient to reduce the actual stress, the result is all too often a negative experience of feeling overwhelmed and unable to make the problem go away, also known as a lack of effective coping. The result of repeated failure to cope with stress is coded in the hippocampus as a trauma memory. As a result, the next time stress is identified the amygdala will likely sound the internal alarm, the hypothalamus releases the CRF and the stress response cycle begins again, often with a similar outcome. Repeated failure to cope with stress can produce chronic or toxic stress and systemic problems throughout the body, only part of which is chronic release of cortisol that kills cells, including neurons. Cortisol also activates glucocorticoid receptor genes making the body more reactive to stress and the myelin basic protein gene which hinders the efficiency of nerve transmission by reducing the insulation on neurons (Weaver, Diorio, Seckl, Szyf & Meaney, 2004).

The above process is called a cycle because there is no end to the brain's picking up stress everywhere in the environment and once a pattern of failed coping is coded in the limbic region of the brain, then the process cycles repeatedly and can become toxic stress. The negative spiral not only includes the perception of being unable to handle the stress in life which impacts self-efficacy in the personality, but a host of other negative factors are produced as a result including: the frequent misperception of threatening stress everywhere, hyper-vigilance, inability to return the arousal system to baseline and inability to turn off the stress response, and undue attention to survival rather than learning and enjoyment. Ultimately toxic stress can break down the body's defenses, such as the immune system, and the door is opened to medical disease.

The structure of the brain can significantly change during stress. It has long been recognized that there is a link between traumatic experience and memory problems. The hypothalamus is the brain's trip wire to recognize and react to stress. Stress releases an additional stress hormone to the three mentioned in Figure 2 and this is glucocorticoid. The release of this stress hormone kills neurons in the hypothalamus. With chronic exposure to stress, such as in repeated childhood traumatic experiences, the hypothalamus shrinks in size. Since the hypothalamus is involved in transforming short-term memory to long-term memory, traumatic experiences impact memory as well. The impact of traumatic experiences on the hypothalamus is only one of many ways the structure of the brain changes with significant stress. However, with this one example of structural changes three important impacts occur: 1. The hypothalamus shrinks in size (Jacobs, van Praag & Gage, 2000), 2. Memories are impaired (Kandel, 2007) and 3. Genes activate the production of glucocorticoid increasing the impact on the hypothalamus creating an additional negative cycle related to stress (Nemeroff, 1996; Heim, Newport, Bonsall, Miller & Nemeroff, 2001).

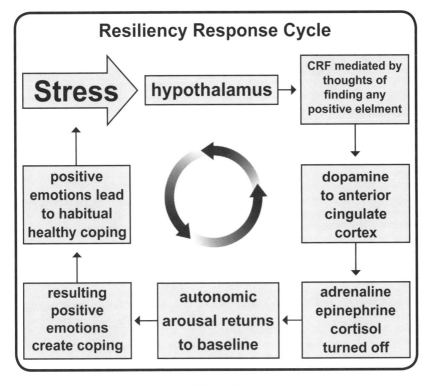

Figure 2

There is an alternative to the experience of habitual and chronic stress response and this alternative is to make a strategic impact primarily at the initiation of the process when the hypothalamus becomes involved. At the point the CRF begins to be released, the prefrontal cortex can influence and override this cycle by giving the situation meaning other than a direct threat to survival. If the prefrontal cortex is successful in 'turning off' the release of CRF, then dopamine (associated with a sense of well-being) is released by the anterior cingulate cortex. With the release of dopamine rather than adrenaline, epinephrine and cortisol, the body's initial activation is reduced and can return to a resting or allostatic state. One term that describes this internal process is relaxation or the reduction of stress toward a more calm state.

The positive benefits of disrupting the stress response cycle does not end with first avoiding toxic stress and second, bringing a reduction of stress and a relaxed state. There is yet another benefit when the individual returns to a state of calm following the release of dopamine, the brain records successful coping in a similar way it records a failure to cope. When the brain registers stress it has been able to cope with in the past, there can be heightened confidence coping is possible, producing more internal confidence. It is often the case if the brain believes it can (or it can't), it is right. When a positive cycle of coping with stress is built up another term for this is resiliency, demonstrated in Figure 2.

In summary, reactions to stress are the key factors in emotional behavioral problems. Turning down the volume and learning how to produce a state of calm is the brain's best weapon in the life-long struggle with stress. One of the best tools to promote coping and eventually resiliency is to find one or more of the many methods of relaxation that will fit best with each individual and build it into the treatment plan.

5. Environmental enhancements promoting the building blocks of brain development

The most effective external impacts on neurological functioning are environmental in nature. The external environment to the child includes people, places and things. For maximum impact, interventions will take advantage of every aspect of the environment. What this specifically means is an intervention in the therapy office (for example using a relaxation technique) will be more effective if a parent uses this approach at home, the teacher at school, and the coach before the game. The message to the child's brain is this is something that will help you regardless of the location, otherwise the brain may associate the ability to relax only with a therapist in an office. Every aspect of the child's world should support the goals of enhancing neurological repair including: family, school, community, church, neighborhood, relatives, scouts, and youth sports among others. Individuals learn attachments and social skills in increasingly widening circles, starting with the mother, then father, then family, then school, then community and so on. In each setting, the child needs to experience success in interacting with the people and environment to broaden the circle of coping, confidence and connection.

Research has supported a number of ingredients that comprise optimal brain change. These ingredients include: 1. Internal motivation, 2. Focused attention, and 3. Repetitive practice (Doidge, 2007). Internal motivation hastens change based upon the saliency of the task and how interested the brain is to put attention to the issue. Focused attention is directly related to internal motivation and these first two ingredients together exercise the brain promoting both growth and adaptation. Attention is important because memory is encouraged in the brain based upon the strength of the signal of the event or information. The more internally interested the person is and the more attention paid to the information, the stronger the corresponding electrical and chemical signals in the brain. Finally, repetitive practice encourages: increased neuronal speed, clarity of signal, efficiency, increased signal strength is more localized and uses less of the brain.

All of the above ingredients can be supported and promoted by external support until internalized. Environmental supports should be in place to provide the building blocks of safety, security, acceptance, belonging, trust, relationship, self- understanding and personal worth throughout the environment the child is in. These building blocks enable the child to build personal growth on a predictable and solid personal foundation. If any environment is traumatic for the child, particularly the family where a foundation must be established, there will likely be problems in other settings as well. Ideally the child can experience the foundation of safety and other building blocks within the child's home to be able to move outward in an expanding circle of social success.

Narrowing the focus to specific interventions the goal is to generalize what the child experiences and learns. We want the child able to transfer the ability to relax from the therapist's office to the classroom and to the shopping mall. We want the child to learn how to handle conflict at home and use these skills with conflict at school. Every skill that will help the child in one environment is likely to help in other settings. Therefore, identify who the adults are in the child's life who may be able to assist with generalizing the skills the child is learning at home and in therapy.

The best interventions to produce the experience of social success are not individual, isolated and brief approaches, but instead are multi-faceted and coordinated approaches involving all aspects of the individual's world. Environmental interventions for a child should include attention to adjustments at home, at school, and expanding involvement in community activities. Many strategies may be used to broaden the impact of therapy into a widening arc in the community, for example, assigning a mentor to the child.

Raising a challenging child is a team sport and the best interventions move outward from the therapy office to the child's life with the assistance of members of the child's team. It is recommended to bring together the key adults in each of the environments that constitute the child's world and work to have everyone on the same page and invested in the same outcome. Teacher may initially resist restructuring the classroom for one student, but when the teacher is invested in the treatment plan and provided with specific approaches to use, the outcome is generally more positive. Adults in professions that work with children want to help but often are not sure how to approach challenging children. At times, every attempt they have made has failed. It is just these situations where the team can provide support to its members and it is more encouraging to be a part of a team effort than feeling like you are alone in trying to reach a difficult child.

The strategies available to encourage neurotransformation are limited only by our imagination. However, there are some standard strategies that should be considered with every individual regardless of the age of the person or the issue of concern. These strategies include:

- Shaping—a process of reinforcing incremental improvement.
- Repetition—concentrated exercise related to the desired change.
- Promoting mental exercise—these exercises enhance the executive functions of the brain as well as enhancing brain change.
- Focus and attention exercises—such activities solidify the internal reward system and promote the nucleus basalis to release acetylcholine which sharpens attention and memory.
- Visualizing change and mental practice—research has shown that brain visualization actually changes the brain in the same way as actual practice (Pascual-Leone, Dang, Cohen, Brasil-Neto, Cammarota & Hallett, 1995; Yue & Cole, 1992).
- Mental focus and thought stopping—it is essential to unlearn problem areas by changing perceptions and thoughts because thoughts are as strong as actions.
- Physical exercise—such activities increase blood flow to the brain, enhance oxygen levels, and stimulate creation of stem cells for brain repair (among many other advantages of physical exercise).
- Cumulative Synergy—mental exercise is linked to social and physical activity bringing the many advantages of these pursuits.

The five steps in this chapter start in a traditional mental health way, but then begin to approach problems from a neurological perspective rather than behavioral or emotional perspective.

These steps can help the typical mistakes made with very difficult children and may help to arrive at a much more positive outcome in the therapy process. The next chapter will build on the last two chapters and outline in very practical detail how Neurological Reparative Therapy informs specific interventions with individual children.

The Five Steps of NRT

Step 1—Determine the extent and causes of the neurological impairment.

Step 2—Identify the cognitive, emotional and behavioral problems that need to change.

Step 3—Implement carefully designed interventions that address the causes of the problem areas.

Step 4—Teach the person to relax and manage the stress of daily life and a complex world.

Step 5—Change the environment as well as the individual for lasting improvement.

Chapter

6

How Neurological Reparative Therapy Informs Interventions

Neurological Reparative Therapy is not an intervention, but can inform interventions. In this chapter the broad conceptual framework of NRT will move to the specific approaches with particular children in a particular situation. The question addressed in this chapter is "Exactly what do I do to help the child I am working with change from the inside out?"

One aspect of the helping professions is to play the role of a problem-solver. As we all know, people are quite skilled at finding themselves in a problem situation with no idea what to do to improve the situation rather than make it worse. At times the problem is not their responsibility, but many times there is only one person to hold accountable and it is the person with the challenge of their own making. Regardless of whose responsibility the situation is, many individuals approach professional problem-solvers to help them out. The various professional disciplines that solve problems include (but are certainly not limited to) medicine, psychology, social work, education, pastoral work, and many others. Effective problem-solving in psychology is somewhat different than other disciplines.

The argument can be made that it does little long-term good to set up an appointment, hear about a problem, hand the client a solution, and set up an appointment for the next week to do it all over again. Some may call this private practice, but it could also be called creating dependency and reducing rather than enhancing self-determination and the ability to make good decisions in life. So this chapter fits the role of psychological problem-solving by modeling a process of problem situations rather than simply offering solutions.

We must start with the acknowledgment that what clients want of therapists is a silver bullet. Even in clinical supervision, new therapists want to learn the answer so they can give it to others. It may initially frustrate the client (and the new therapist) to hear that the answer to the problem is only useful in a particular situation and, therefore, less important than learning the process of how to solve problems. In other words, a characteristic of a good therapist is being an artist rather than a technician. People are complex and when they get together, such as in a family or social network, the complexity geometrically expands. The quick answer is often not the best answer. The best answer to a problem comes from taking the time to fully consider the situation and its complexity. Therefore this chapter is about a process of coming up with solutions.

Most professional problem-solvers, particularly those with a lot of experience, tend to see similarities in the problems that are brought to them. Therapists often make associations between the past and the present. However, bringing too much of the past into the present often hampers the professional problem-solver by cutting short the process of full consideration of the individual and the circumstance. As a psychologist who does family therapy, I once believed that there were only about twelve types of problems I would see. During this period, I would listen to the parent and the child and quickly I could see that this was a category #11, which reminded me of past cases and the solution I previously used that worked and then suggest these approaches. This approach was informed by experience, it was quick, it was efficient and it was wrong.

For a variety of reasons, solutions and interventions with one person do not generalize in effectiveness to another. Interventions with one person often do not generalize to the same person the next time the problem comes up. We must all work to avoid the neat and tidy categories of problem solutions that we offer people. I believe this is one reason why I hear so often, "We have been to many professionals and none have been able to help us." These professionals wanted to be of help but the complexity of the most challenging individuals eliminates the ability to categorize and offer formula solutions. So it may only be the most challenging and complex cases that need the process of developing interventions that will be discussed, but this is doubtful. Each and every time a therapist is faced with a challenging problem, the more consideration of the issue and the circumstances, the more there can be an understanding of the dynamics of the individuals involved and the better therapists can teach individuals how to find their own effective solutions. In the long run, encouraging self-determination may result in less of a need to setup an appointment with the professional problem-solver. I was taught in my graduate program to begin each case with the goal to eliminate the need for the client to have to come to you. I don't know if this is still taught in graduate school since I do not hear this from new graduates, but I believe it is still important to promote self-determination and instill inner confidence in the client to plot their own course through troubled waters.

Categorizing the problems of clients is not the only mistake that therapists and behavioral workers make. For a variety of reasons including being in a hurry, past experience, and wanting to find the solution and move on, the common process of developing an intervention goes from finding the problem to moving to a solution. When we do this we take a short cut that often results in us getting lost on the journey to the true solution.

Neurological Reparative Therapy is a framework to understand how the brain operates and the best outcomes are those that come from within. Therefore, what is going on inside the individual is where the task of finding effective interventions will succeed or fail. Believing you know the answer as soon as you hear the problem does not take into consideration the unique way this individual's brain is perceiving this situation. Nor does it take into consideration the past experiences of the individual, which often leads to some predictable emotions and behaviors. NRT informs interventions by insuring that these internal factors of the individual's cognitive and affective processing are taken into consideration.

The following diagram reflects what often takes place in developing interventions. The problem is identified and the proposed solutions are not far behind. However, there are two critical steps in the problem-solving process that are often either ignored or not given sufficient attention — what is the meaning of the target symptom to the client and what are the causes.

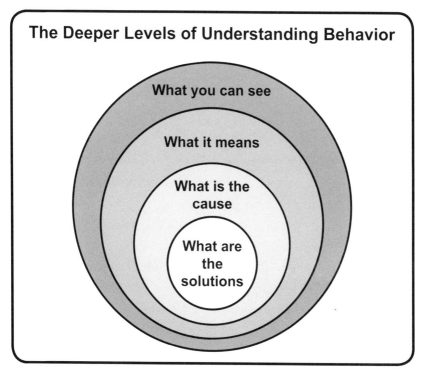

Figure 3

Problem Identification or What You Observe

Most adults who deal with difficult children believe the easiest step in the process of addressing problems is to determine what the problem is and they are wrong. This has long been recognized in medicine where considerable time goes into the correct diagnosis leading to the right treatment and a successful intervention if the diagnosis is accurate. However, when it comes to human behavior, particularly children, too often adults assume that what you see is what you get. This assumption leads to a belief that the problem is the child's tantrums, or perhaps it is the child's sexual behavior, or it is an anger problem that results in violence. However, many times if an intervention is developed for problems like these, success may be elusive because what we see is often an outgrowth of the problem but not the true problem. Medical practice often has an advantage over psychological practice in that treating the symptom often works. However, the brain makes the problem behavior of people much more complex than what meets the eye.

As in medicine, it is essential to successful interventions to first identify the correct problem. The entire process will help determine the correct problem and, in the meantime, the first step is to carefully consider the target behavior. It is important to be specific and detailed. For example, saying the problem is the child's moodiness is far too general, whereas saying the child becomes angry and aggressive when given correction by an adult female is more specific and more helpful. So, the first step in the process is to identify a specific, observable target symptom.

What the Behavior Means to the Child

Once a target symptom has been specifically identified, it is important to ask what the behavior means to the individual. All behavior has meaning and it may take a bit of detective work to find out what the meaning is to the person. Do not skip this step, it is the most critical aspect of finding effective interventions.

I have described this step in my other books as translating the child's behavior (Ziegler, 2000). As in all translations, the goal is to find the meaning. In this case the goal is to find the meaning of the behavior to this child. A couple of questions that may help this process are: "What is the child saying to us by her behavior?" "What is the meaning of this behavior to the child?" Many adults come up short at this point and say, "How am I supposed to know, the child doesn't even know?" This may be true that the child is not fully aware of what he is saying through what he is doing, but that should not stop us from putting the puzzle pieces together.

It is at this point in the process that an exercise may help to determine the most accurate translation of the child's behavior. There is a dynamic I refer to as the child speaking in opposites. This is a pattern I observed many years ago when I worked primarily with teens, when I frequently found that teens said things to their parents that were different than they told me, their therapist. A teen would say to a parent in family therapy something like, "Why do you always have to grill me when I am going somewhere? I hate it when you do that!" This being the opposite of what the teen had indicated to me earlier in private when he said, "My friend has parents who are too busy to be bothered, he stays out all night and they do not even know. I'm glad my parents care what I am up to." From this observation that occurred on many occasions, I began to see the difference between what a young person is saying and what the real meaning may be. This pattern that I first observed in teens began to be apparent with challenging children. Speaking in opposites is not always the case, however, so it is important to consider what the real meaning may be in a particular situation.

Here is an exercise that could help, write down as many verbalizations as you can remember that the child frequently says, particularly when she is anxious and under stress. If you have a teen your list might look something like this, consider the opposite (in italics) and see which is closer to what the young person is really saying:

- Stop bothering me, I hate it! *I am scared that I am starting to like it that you give me attention.*

- You just don't understand me! *You see right through me and I feel exposed around you.*
- I wish I was not in this family. *I feel comfortable here and that means I have a lot to lose.*
- You are the world's worst parent by far! *No one has been there for me like you have been and it frightens me.*
- I am not worried about my future, bring it on! *What am I going to do when I don't have my parents to fight with.*

If you have a young child, the list may look more like this:

- You are mean to me because you hate me! *I am beginning to feel cared for and I am scared.*
- School is stupid. *I don't want anyone to find out what I don't know, it is me who is stupid.*
- I hate everyone in this family. *I feel like I belong here and what happens if you send me away.*
- You are a bad cook, I liked my mom's food. *I really like your meals but I must be loyal to my neglectful mother.*
- Don't touch me, it feels gross! *Being touched feels good and bad at the same time; I am more comfortable with it feeling bad.*

Do this exercise about the child you are interested in. List the most common statements that come out of his or her mouth and focus on the negative expressions that often feel hurtful. Now put the opposite next to the list as was done above. Read one list and then read the other, which list contains more truth? This will tell you if your child speaks in opposites when he or she is under stress. Not all children do this and some children do so only some of the time. However, if the child is speaking in opposites, don't let the negative messages hurt you, instead hear the real message without requiring the child to put it in words they are not yet strong enough to say to you.

What are the Causes of the Behavior?

Behaviors are the result of complex processes in the brain. The behavior you see, whether a problem or not, comes from the mental process of how the individual perceives a situation. This perceptual system is often an important part of what needs to change. Based upon the individual's perception, the person assigns meaning to a situation. The brain will act not upon the situation but the meaning given to the situation. It is often the case that problem behaviors are rooted in misperceptions of either what has taken place or the motivations of people involved in what has taken place.

After meaning is determined by the individual, the person has an emotional response to this meaning. For example, just before writing this a child was asked a question by an adult who had no energy in the issue and there was no loaded meaning in the question. However, the child believed the adult was trying to trick him into revealing something so the adult could then criticize the child. It was the perception of the event that determined the child's behavior, which in this case was the initiation of the stress response cycle. Stress signals to the pituitary and adrenal glands of the body to send hormones through the circulatory system preparing for a fight or flight response for self-protection. In this case, the child shut down all verbal and bodily activity and dissociated into a frozen state. The adult was first surprised by the response, then confused, then frustrated leading to disappointment. This is a good example of the process of perception assigning meaning and developing an emotional response going both ways. In this case while the child misperceived the situation, the child's response led to the adult misperceiving the situation as well.

Denise's Self-Harm

Denise was referred to the program for a myriad of reasons among which were her self-harmful behavior and apparent self-hatred. She had previously swallowed glass, sprayed herself in the face with cleaning chemicals, and repeatedly referenced wanting to die. This pattern of behavior, which over time had evolved into negative attention-seeking and forced engagement, continued early on in the program, with Denise punching herself in the face, attempting to ingest non-edible objects, intentionally hitting her head against walls or the floor, biting herself, and vocalizing feelings of worthlessness aimed at provoking staff intervention. Denise required a great deal of support, positive reflections of herself, and opportunities for success in order to develop a more positive identity, paired with clear limits related to her self-harm. With this treatment over time, Denise became increasingly proud of herself, and could list multiple positive assets, including her athleticism which she commented she had not previously known existed. Not only her emotions and behaviors changed, but her body emerged from an obese child to a fit and healthy preteen. She was even able to reach her goal of running more than 80 miles in the summer jogging program. Of equal importance, Denise became more self-aware related to her pattern of attention-seeking and began to exhibit capacity for interrupting the negative cycle, instead seeking out support appropriately or initiating her own self-regulatory processes. She graduated from the program a different young lady on every level.

Shannon Sell, MSW, CSWA

The final step in the process from perception to an emotional response is an externalized behavior that can be seen and often heard. Therefore when we want to address a problem behavior, we need to understand that the perceptions of everyone involved (including you) must be taken into account.

The causes of the target symptom also have roots in the past. For this reason it is very helpful to know as much as possible about the previous experiences of a child. Often there is a clue from the past to explain current behavior. The past is directly linked to perceptual issues due to the limbic region of the brain that impacts a number of brain functions including traumatic memory, fear activation, and emotional disposition. With this combination, past traumatic or even negative experiences are recalled; anxiety, stress and fear are signaled; and behaviors often on the continuum of fight or flight are produced — all within the limbic region of the brain. It is for this reason that it can be said traumatized individuals have very well-developed limbic regions at the determent of development in the orbitofrontal cortex where executive functions are centered.

What are the Solutions — Finding Effective Interventions

The quick and most common method of developing interventions is to notice a problem and come up with a solution or intervention. This can work with most children but it often falls far short with challenging children. You will notice the difference when nothing you do seems to work with a particular child. The solution to being ineffective with your interventions is to take the time to consider the other steps after you identify the problem — translate the behavior and find what it means to the child, then consider the likely causes of the behavior. Now you are in a much better position to come up with interventions that have a chance to work. You may come up with a sophisticated and impressive solution, but if you are working on the wrong problem it will be of little use.

Developing interventions is not the end of the journey, but more like the start. The parent of a troubled child will need to learn to become an expert at coming up with interventions for this specific child because it is a task that must be done thousands of times before the child is an adult (and even then it does not stop). Get familiar with the process and don't become attached to any particular intervention, some work and some don't. Either way move on and get better each time you go through the process. If an intervention does not work, follow the procedure in this book and come up with another. Don't dwell on either the ones that work or the ones that fail, the point is not your win and loss record but your ability to help your child. Even if you have the ideal intervention in this situation, it may not work the next time. Learn how to be resilient in addressing problems with your child or your client. Bounce back when something does not work and see this as a new opportunity to get better at problem-solving.

This brief explanation of the process of developing interventions can now be placed into a protocol that takes one step at a time.

Neurological Reparative Therapy – Intervention Protocol

The fundamental principle underlying Neurological Reparative Therapy is the recognition that the child's brain is the target of all interventions. Perceptions, emotions and behaviors are all the outgrowth of the perceptual system and neurological processing of the child's brain. The following is the protocol to assist in developing interventions to facilitate the repair of neurological processes within the child. Every child is different and every situation is different, and adjustments should be made to individualize every effort to develop effective interventions.

Step 1 – Be specific as to the target symptom (problem behavior) to be the focus of the intervention.

Most children have a variety of problem behaviors or issues that need to be addressed. It is critical that one behavior at a time is worked on. Avoid global statements of the target symptom such as: he never complies, she is continually oppositional, she shows poor social skills. Be specific, what behavior? When does it happen? Pick the best location to work on the issue.

Step 2 – Translate the meaning of the behavior.

All behavior has meaning. Frequently the meaning is not obvious and may be counterintuitive. For example, it is important to consider how children with emotional disturbances speak in opposites (for example, "Get away from me!" often means, "I need your help right now."). There are three parts to translating.

First, ask what the meaning of the behavior is to the child. How is he perceiving the situation and how does the child's response fit with his perceptions of the environment?

Second, make a list of possible translations of the identified behavior. Violence in science class may mean: the child is bored, wants individual attention, is worried about tomorrow's visit, or he might be communicating I need tighter structure, particularly if he is verbalizing he hates the rules. Identify at least ten possible translations of the behavior. When the translation step is addressed it is helpful to use your intuitive reasoning and be as creative as possible. An approach I find helpful, particularly with professionals who can get into a linear or logical rut in their thinking, is to identify one or two possible translations that are a real stretch, something far afield or something that has never been considered. The purpose of doing this is to think more broadly and creatively. The impact of doing this step can be significant. It is not unusual to have the more bizarre translations actually help in informing the interventions.

Third, make a list of the things the child frequently says, particularly when she has strong energy or is under some stress. Make a column with the frequent statements. Now take each statement and write down the opposite of the statement. Read both lists and determine which is a more truthful statement for this child. For children who often speak in opposites, this exercise will help you be more clear about what the child's actual message to you is. When it comes to translating a child's message, the actual words are often the least helpful aspect of the communication. Children and adults most often communicate their primary message with non-verbal communication, energy level and how they use the words rather than the words themselves.

Step 3 – Identify any environmental influences that may be causing the target symptom.

It is important to know the child's trauma history and other aspects of the child's past to determine the perceptions of what the child is currently experiencing. Being able to see the situation from the child's perspective is critical to being able to understand the meaning of the target symptom to the child, or at least to the child's brain.

Step 4 – Develop interventions that address as many aspects of the child's daily environment as possible.

After the first three steps, it is possible to come up with solutions to the real problem rather than aspects of the problem. Professionals who go through this protocol often get to this step and become anxious because they don't want to get it wrong. This anxiety is a hindrance to the process of creative interventions. We don't use our full cognitive creativity when we are afraid to make a mistake. Make a list of potential interventions before narrowing them down to the ones that you want to implement or want to try first. Develop a macro view before arriving at the micro intervention. The more ideas the better, and the more creative the better. Even if an unusual intervention may miss the mark, it is likely to confuse the defenses of the child and alter the power differential in your favor.

When developing a list of interventions keep in mind that the environment is the most important influence on the child. Interventions that impact home, school, and community settings are more effective than those in only one setting. So have interventions on your list that can be implemented at school, at home, in the neighborhood, at church, and at Grandma's house.

Step 5 – Decide on measures that will indicate if the developed intervention is having the desired impact.

This is the evaluation step. Do not be concerned if your initial efforts to address a problem seem a little half-baked or questionable. You should know what your hope is for progress and you can evaluate whether you are headed in the right direction. Keep in mind that with children who have emotional or behavioral disturbances, when you have the right issue and even the right intervention, the initial response may well be that things get worse before they start getting better, so expect this rather than be discouraged by it. Sometimes it is just the wrong idea or the wrong approach. This should not be discouraging, but instead lead us back to the process to look for a translation and intervention that may come closer to the target.

The problem is not only interventions that may be dead wrong or even make the problem worse, but interventions that work may be problematic. Sometimes we strike gold and the intervention works like a charm. However, give the child some time to consider what has happened and be prepared that the problem comes roaring back and the perfect intervention yesterday has the opposite effect today. It is anticipated that the initial result of this process may need modification even if it is initially effective. Therefore, determine a time frame (a day, a week, a month, etc.) after which data related to the measures (points, violent incidents, bedtimes, etc.) will be reviewed to track movement. Nearly all interventions with seriously disturbed children will need frequent adjustments. Maintain your energy and look at this process as a long distance marathon where there will be many steps along the way and miles to go before the race has been run.

To prevent this intervention protocol from appearing too complex or difficult to follow, in the next chapter specific case examples will be provided to make it as clear as possible. However, even if the task is clear, we nearly always need to practice a new skill until we become proficient at it.

NRT Informs Interventions

Behavior must be understood at the neurological level and it is now possible to do so.

The problem behavior that can be observed is only the tip of the iceberg.

The meaning of the behavior to the person is important to understand, it may not be obvious.

The causes of the behavior are important since the brain functions on past experience.

Only after determining the meaning and the causes can effective interventions be developed.

Targeted and comprehensive interventions are the key to changing the brain.

Chapter

7

Neurological Reparative Therapy in Practice – Case Example of Improving Neuro-Integration

For most people the best way to understand a concept is to see it in action or have it put into a practical context. This is what this chapter will do. The first of three children will be discussed including a brief background, problematic behaviors, and finally how Neurological Reparative Therapy informed the direction of treatment, including the NRT intervention model. A fully detailed description of treatment will not be given for each child. Instead a different aspect of the process will be emphasized for each individual. The following cases are real children with only minor changes (such as names) incorporated in the information to protect the confidentiality of the child and family.

Sheryl

With the first case example, the causes of the problem areas will be emphasized along with the overall direction of treatment. Born in a small town in a western state, Sheryl (age 9) had two immediate challenges to her healthy development – nature and nurture. Her genetics were not ideal in that in her immediate and extended family mental health problems were abundant. These issues included bipolar disorder, addictions, a family member with pedophilia, several members with attention deficit hyperactive disorder and a family trait of chronic depression.

As a result of some of the mental problems that were present in the family, Sheryl had to also face a cold and aloof affect among family members, including her mother. She was fed and clothed but since no one in the family felt particularly special, they were unable to give any sense of being special to little Sheryl. Her parents were not demonstrative with each other except when it came to negative emotions. Although domestic violence in a physical form was not a part of the family, frequent outbursts of anger and verbal frustration were a daily occurrence. Over time family members learned that interpersonal contact most often led to negative outcomes rather than support and comfort. Due to this unspoken dynamic, family members lived their lives in proximity with each other but for the most part alone. As with all children, Sheryl's developing brain adjusted to this environment.

The extended family was important in this household because several family members lived close to each other and contact was frequent. Sheryl's parents lived unhappily together very similar to Sheryl's maternal grandparents who lived unhappily together not far away. One paternal uncle and a paternal aunt and an unmarried maternal uncle all lived close enough to have frequent although generally unhealthy contact with each other. There was also a lack of appropriate boundaries among family members with everyone having knowledge of and expressing their opinions of each other's frequent problems and issues. The combination of family mental health problems and poor social involvement led to an overall tone of unpredictable chaos and unhealthy expressions of mostly negative emotions. The overall atmosphere in this large family network was that something bad was always about to happen, and there was little ability within the family to either resolve problems or even tolerate each other. The frequent expressions of anger or intolerance resulted in a familial characteristic of a lack of closeness or attachment with each other. Little emotional congruence could be found with family members. Family members fought and criticized each other but provided little comfort or support to each other. Sheryl was no exception as she grew up. Often times mental health disorders can be reflected in a person's appearance. Meeting Sheryl's extended family provided a clear sense that there were both organic as well as social deficiencies in Sheryl's gene pool.

We are all a sum total of the influences on our brains. Sheryl had a rather unusual presentation in several ways. She stood out among other children in a way that you could pick her out of a group due to the unusual way she acted. Although she would interact with other children, they found her aloof and odd. When children pick up unusual energy from other children, this is often cause to avoid or tease and make fun of the unusual child and this was frequently the situation with Sheryl.

Sheryl had 'soft' signs of a number of mental health issues. She did not meet the full diagnostic criteria for Attention Deficit and yet she was unfocused and unable to keep her attention on a subject for any extended period of time. She made poor interpersonal contact with adults and peers. One minute she would be doing fine interacting with someone, and the next minute she might start staring blankly and she seemed unaware she was doing this. Her emotional expressions were muted although at times she could express happiness and joy and at other times sadness. Her emotions were like the rest of her overall presentation around others, she was not consistent and seemed to change her interests, attention and feelings frequently and often in an unexpected direction.

Sheryl was the kind of child who might slip between the cracks of our educational and mental health system except for one thing, she was often difficult to manage for adults. Sheryl was not a violent child but she was disruptive and a behavioral challenge due to her frequent outbursts of being silly and uninterested in attending to what was going on around her. This may have developed as a coping style from frequently being confused and not understanding much of what was going on around her. Her outbursts of silly, over-the-top inappropriate laughter made it difficult for others, adults and children, to interact with Sheryl.

Sheryl did not do well in school and often seemed lost and confused. She seemed to accept this state of confusion and usually did not express strong negative emotions when confused, as if to indicate that she found this state familiar and not at all unusual. The many higher order cognitive skills making up the list of executive functions were poorly developed and intermittent. The result of her poor cognitive functioning resulted in serious learning problems. Her academic progress was similar to her behavioral and emotional presentation in that she was variable and did not learn in a linear fashion. She did not appear to learn from her experiences. She made some gains only to appear to lose these skills the next time she needed them. An overall observation was that Sheryl had low cognitive functions, which would explain most of her presentation except for one major issue — she tested at the above average range of cognitive ability.

The results of her first cognitive testing were something of a shock to her clinical team. With confirmation of low cognitive ability much of Sheryl's presentation could be explained. Even if she was tested on the wrong day or experiencing personal anxiety, she could achieve a score in the borderline range of cognitive functioning. But when tested in optimal conditions, it became clear that Sheryl had considerable cognitive ability. With her above average intelligence, the mystery of her many problem issues remained. If she did not struggle from poor cognitive ability, then what would explain her many mental processing issues?

Sheryl's Problem was a Deficiency of Neurological Integration

Considering all the factors, there was only one good explanation for the issues Sheryl was struggling with, and that was that she had a brain with components that had the ability to function well but the regions of the brain were not working in tandem with each other. Sheryl had normal memory but was unable to use her memory of the past to inform her next decision. She had a good fund of knowledge, she was just unable to put her knowledge to good use. She understood what needed to be done in school, she was just unable to focus on the task long enough to accomplish it. All of these issues are symptomatic of a deficiency of neuro-integration.

If neuro-integration was the problem, then what caused it? The answer to this question likely included both genetic as well as environmental influences. Sheryl came from a family where the modeling was consistent with her issues. She appeared to be unable to appropriately handle her stress with her silly outbursts and this was probably caused by the lack of initial attachment that is needed for internal self-regulation. The early insecure attachment also appeared to affect her connection with others, a theme within her family. Although she was born with parts of her brain capable of learning and developing, there may have been genetic influences resulting in her brain struggling with internal communication. While there may well have been genetic causes for her deficiencies, her problems could also be impacted by environmental influences such as modeling by family members.

The right and left hemispheres both have important jobs to do, but just because there is good communication does not mean there is fully developed coordination of mental activity. For mental cohesion some part of the brain must decide what to focus on and what to ignore as well as instructing mental operations that lead toward a certain goal. This is the job of the brain's chief executive officer or the decision-maker of the brain. This role is fulfilled by areas of the frontal cortex and specifically the orbitofrontal cortex.

The orbitofrontal cortex is positioned in the brain to maximize connections with all other sections of the brain. When explaining this to children, it can be described as the place where the pilot sits in an airplane, on top of the front part of the plane. The flight deck of a plane is analogous to the human brain at the top front of the person where all wiring leads. A plane can be in perfect working order but it still needs a pilot to make the components work together to safety and efficiently function.

The deficiencies that were apparent in Sheryl were precisely the functions of the orbitofrontal cortex. These functions include:

- Mental flexibility—Sheryl demonstrated a serious lack of having mental processes that changed course, adapted to situations, or modified out of the necessity of conditions that changed around her. Either her environment had to accommodate to her or she was lost and went into her familiar dissociative confusion.

- Wide range of emotional expression—Sheryl was able to show a restrictive range of emotions but they were seldom appropriate to the situation. She could laugh, cry, become angry and seemed pleased, but each of these could be expressed at times where they would be unexpected and did not follow from events around her. For example, she would laugh loudly when other children were quiet in class or she might cry and there appeared to be no apparent cause. Both her range of emotions and congruency of her affective states were problem areas.

- Autobiographical memory—Sheryl's most distinguishing personal characteristic and what seemed to form much of her personality was a lack of a sense of self. The continuity of self develops primarily in the prefrontal cortex and this comes from an internal knowledge of the past and what has made us who we are. This important sense of self was undeveloped.

- Forming successful social attachments with others— Sheryl came from a family with poor interpersonal skills. Connection often meant conflict and therefore in this family environment things went smoother if connection with other family members was skillfully avoided. Sheryl grew up with this tone around her and therefore tended to become anxious and irritable when she did interpersonally connect with peers and adults. Her connections could not be considered successful attachments and therefore she missed out on all the many advantages of attachment including social support, a sense of belonging, and being a part of something greater than the self.

There is a causal link between the development of attachment and the development of the orbitofrontal cortex. Either both mature simultaneously or the lack of development in one produces delayed development in the other. In Sheryl's case both the development of positive interpersonal attachments and her orbitofrontal cortex were showing deficiencies. Because of these delays, she would be expected to have poor self-awareness and this was the case. Her poor social interactions appeared to be caused by a lack of understanding of the intentions and motivations of the people around her. She tended to avoid connection with others and when others initiated she was prepared for conflict, consistent with her experience in her family.

Without a developed orbitofrontal cortex, Sheryl was often unable to understand the meaning of events around her. She had learned an adaptive response to being confused and bewildered and that was to dissociate into a distant and aloof state. This was a learned response to prevent the frequent excitation of the autonomic nervous system whenever she was confused. The dissociative adaptation helped to turn off the unpleasant anxiety of confusion by simply leaving confusion behind. However, when she became spacey and in a dissociative state, she left behind not only her anxiety and discomfort, she left behind other people and her experience of life around her. Sheryl needed help to more fully develop both attachments and the orbitofrontal cortex in order to help her obtain mental coherence and the cohesive coordination of the different parts of her brain.

Sheryl was not just missing life and people around her, she was also reflecting problematic expressions of emotions and behaviors. She spent much of her time either in her aloof state of being distant and spacey, or she was anxious and irritable. Therefore she had the choice of either being disconnected with herself or in a state of negative emotions. Without a secure attachment either early in life or at present, and without a developed decision maker (orbitofrontal cortex), Sheryl lacked the ability to self-regulate what came into and out of her own brain. She was unable to prioritize sensory input leading her to be frequently overwhelmed and confused by the thousands of sensory signals coming into her brain when they did not come to a developed control center. Her brain effectively picked up sensory input, but it was as if she experienced an alarm clock going off simultaneously with a police siren and a fire alarm. Normal input coming into her brain was simply overwhelming to her. One of many negative results of the deficiency of self-regulation was her frequent displays of negative emotional and behavioral outbursts. Sheryl was a very confused and unhappy young girl, ill-suited for the world and the prospects for her future did not bode well because she did not have the building blocks of good mental health.

How Sheryl's Neuro-integration was Repaired

Knowing that Sheryl's brain was showing ineffective internal communication, was there a way to improve this situation? In Sheryl's case the answer to this question was yes, although this may not be the case for all children like Sheryl. The challenge was to help the components of Sheryl's brain work in harmony to develop skills and functioning that would allow her to be successful in daily life. The second challenge was to assist her to avoid information and sensory overload by more fully developing her ability to screen out sensory input that was superfluous to what she needed to consider. The direction of treatment would be to enhance neuro-integration within Sheryl's disorganized brain, and to simultaneously develop a decision-maker in her prefrontal cortex that could help her form meaning from the multitude of inputs and operations within her brain.

The advantage of improved neuro-integration for Sheryl would be improved stability, flexibility and adaptability. These three ingredients would be essential in providing her a much needed sense of well-being. Although neuro-integration pulls together many aspects of the brain, a very good place to start this process is improving inter-hemispheric communication. Sheryl's left and right brains needed to do a better job communicating and working together. The right side of her brain would ideally handle non-verbal communication, perceptual understanding, emotional expression, regulating her nervous system and social connections. The left hemisphere would normally handle linear processes, linguistic expression, logical thinking, cause and effect awareness, and moral reasoning. Helping Sheryl would first of all need to involve bringing the two hemispheres into a collaborative unit.

There are many ways that right and left hemispheric communication can be enhanced. In Sheryl's situation a few interventions were the primary focus. During therapy sessions Sheryl was frequently asked if she had feelings around the topics of discussion. To facilitate this exploration, the therapist would intentionally address sensitive issues starting with content not directly related to Sheryl, but over time moving closer to sensitive issues for her. If Sheryl was aware of any feelings, she was asked to describe them in as much detail as she could. Her right hemisphere was the source of the feelings and the left hemisphere had to be used to describe them. She was also asked to close her eyes and listen to music while simultaneously forming an image in her mind of what the music made her think about. While this was going on Sheryl was asked to describe the images or thoughts she was having.

The right hemisphere is also responsible for social connections. Once again in therapy Sheryl was asked to explain her understanding of what was going on between her and the therapist, both when they were enjoying the time together and when she was frustrated or confused about the interaction. These interventions were chosen because they exercised both right and left hemispheres while requiring both to work in unison. Each time this would happen new neuropathways were developed and strengthened.

The premise underlying the treatment approach for Sheryl was that her two hemispheres were not effectively working in unison. The likely cause of this problem may have centered in the underdeveloped or damaged corpus callosum , which is the main communication link between the two hemispheres of her brain. This part of the brain is often negatively affected by traumatic, neglectful or chaotic environments in the early years of a child's life. While the corpus callosum is critical for inter-hemispheric communication, once the two brains begin to effectively have information exchange, there is one more important part of the brain that leads to integration — the orbitofrontal cortex.

Fortunately as neuro-integration is enhanced, the decision-making region of the brain, the orbitofrontal cortex, is also developing. The more experience and practice, the more it develops and learns to effectively perform its very necessary functions. It would only be through a strong orbitofrontal cortex that Sheryl would learn to prioritize sensory information and thus overcome her constant state of being overwhelmed leading to a need to dissociate to cope with the anxiety and discomfort. While deficiencies in attachment, decision-making and in the integration of mental operations can all work against an individual such as Sheryl, the reverse is also true. Improvement in one area can have corresponding improvements in other areas.

Sheryl had an underdeveloped ability to bond and attach with others, and the ability to do this was an important aspect of her treatment. To assist with attachment skills, Sheryl not only had the same therapist throughout her intensive treatment but she was also assigned a personal mentor whose job was to develop a friendship with her. Sheryl began to experience a different quality of connecting with others that was characterized by support and comfort rather than conflict and anxiety. She began to like the time her therapist and mentor spent with her and she looked forward to these opportunities.

Barry Learned to Move on From His Painful Past

Barry had been in State custody since he was two due to neglect and abuse, and things did not improve when removed from his home into State care. He was in fifteen different placements in a six year period where he was further abused, both physically and sexually. Upon reaching Jasper Mountain, he was in the midst of traumatic memories, family anxiety issues, and significant reactive attachment concerns. Caregivers and families in the past had harmed him and his life schema was that it was safer to aggressively avoid relationships rather than being abused or being rejected all over again. It took time but over months in the treatment program he addressed his anger and past abuse and slowly let others care for and support him. When Barry had changed his perception of adults, he graduated into a treatment foster family and continued to improve. Through difficult months of treatment, confronting his past abuse and his negative thinking patterns, and more than a little violent acting out along the way, Barry changed from within. The treatment process was difficult on him and everyone around him, but he emerged not just a survivor but a different person. After graduating from treatment he eliminated his violence, developed friends, and was proud to say, "My life is way better now!" The past still hurts when he thinks about it, but it no longer has the same hold on him.

Alex Hager, M.A.

With seriously impaired neurological functioning such as Sheryl's, attachment was only one of many issues that had to be addressed. Sheryl's memory appeared to be lacking from a practical standpoint. She scored close to normal on her memory functioning, but practically she did not use her memory to the degree she needed to. This would look like her inability to remember events or instructions that she had recently experienced. The primary problem in her practical application of memory capacity was her lack of attention to events around her. Her brain regarded much of what went on around her as unimportant. In our recalling events, the situations that are salient or impactful and important are the ones we typically remember. For example, where we first heard about the bombing of the World Trade Center will likely be remembered while what we had for dinner on September 8th or September 10th of 2001 have much less significance. Sheryl's memory problem was that she ascribed little meaning to events and they were not stored in either her short or long-term memory.

The treatment to improve her memory was to make events more important to her. Memory is enhanced by making associations between two things. Linking one concept with another enhances recall. Sheryl was helped to see events as more meaningful and she learned to link two things together to help remember both.

Sheryl had very poor self-awareness and in particular she had a poor sense of her external and internal bodily awareness. For example, she might wait until she nearly had an accident before realizing she needed to use the restroom. She would eat until someone told her to stop rather than picking up the sensory information that she was feeling full. Her proprioception, or her understanding of spatial issues and how she occupied the space around her, was very poor. This resulted in a pronounced clumsiness, running into objects and people and a lack of understanding what her arms and legs were doing at the same time. This more advanced sensory issue comes from multiple parts of the brain and requires internal brain communication that Sheryl lacked.

A final major issue was understanding and having congruent affective expression. Sheryl might laugh at sad events or seem confused when something was humorous. This trait of incongruence in affect was explained after brief contacts with her family. Anger might be expressed when a family member said he did not feel angry. Serious statements might be met with laughter from one of more family members. In part, the problem with her emotional expression was her environment influences. The best treatment for this was to place her in repeated situations where she observed and was helped to have emotions fit the situation along with helping her understand what was going on inside of her.

Autobiographical Narrative

Who we are is a combination of our experience, our genetic makeup, our upbringing and our internal sense of self that can be called an autobiographical narrative. Everyone is aware of personal preferences, I like milk chocolate rather than dark bittersweet chocolate or I prefer vanilla rather than chocolate milkshakes. But who is the 'I' who has these preferences, and where is the 'I' inside the brain? The best answer is that the integration of all aspects of self-awareness within the brain come together in the prefrontal cortex where memories and a cumulative sense of self develops into an internal sense of 'I am' or 'I like or dislike.' The less developed the orbitofrontal cortex is, the less of a sense of self or autobiographical narrative the individual has. Without this sense of self, we have a limited life story and a limited awareness of a consistent internal self.

Autobiographical narratives are important components of trauma treatment. Our narratives of self are formed with both positive and negative life events. Trauma can impair the autobiographical narrative. Sheryl needed help in more fully developing her narrative regarding her past and her present. One approach used with Sheryl was techniques to help her recall her past, understand and focus on her present and to expand this to have her consider her future. This was done both in individual therapy and in group therapy with children who were having similar challenges.

We could assist Sheryl to better understand herself, to put more focus on events around her and improve her working memory if we could help her with affective congruence and improve the integration of all the various components of her brain producing neuro-integration. Then the hope was to see more mental and emotional flexibility to adapt to events in Sheryl's life. We also would expect to see an improvement in focus and her brain's ability to heal itself after stressful or emotional events. Is that what happened?

Results of Sheryl's Treatment

At the point it was clear that Sheryl's presentation of having low cognitive ability was more accurately a problem of neuro-integration, her treatment was adjusted accordingly in the directions outlined above. It was clear that the adults around Sheryl would need to change their perceptions of her before we could help change her self-perception. While she had a number of significant gaps in her mental and emotional functioning, she also had many untapped mental abilities. With help in improving her sense of self and the world around her, her emotional incongruence was one of the first improvements noticed. She became more emotional, she cried more and she laughed more, but it was genuine laughter and not confused feelings that she habitually expressed by a silly laugh that was not genuine. She also reflected a wider range of genuine feelings, a trait associated with better mental health.

The next improvement noticed was an increased focus, especially in school. With an improvement in focus and being on task, her medications were reduced resulting in a more genuine connection with others, both positive and negative. She began to improve in academic areas and her mental abilities that were for the most part dormant began to awaken and she liked the result. Sheryl began to develop a better sense of her strengths and she reflected a growing sense of liking herself. In other words, her autobiographical narrative was becoming more detailed and more positive.

At the point that Sheryl's problem was identified as a lack of a developed orbitofrontal cortex and poor neuro-integration, the treatment began in earnest and improvements were not far behind. Within less than six months, Sheryl had improved to the point of being able to function appropriately in a family setting and she began to see some of the deficient patterns in her own family. When her treatment concluded, Sheryl was the most functional member of her family in many respects. Her challenges were not over, particularly in her family environment, but she had a better developed sense of herself in contrast to other family members, and these new mental and emotional skills were being put to use with her family and with peers around her. At the conclusion of her treatment, Sheryl had a much better potential to use her brain in productive ways heading into her future.

Case Example—Repairing Neuro-Integration

Signs pointing to a problem with neuro-integration: poor mental flexibility, restricted emotions, lack of autobiographical memory, and poor social connectedness.

Poor neuro-integration can look like low cognitive functioning.

Teach the brain to work as a unit by starting with coordination of the left and right hemispheres.

Improving attachment can assist the brain to have better internal communication.

Use exercises to improve memory.

Help children tune into body sensations for better self-awareness.

Integrate past and present experience to improve the autobiographical narrative.

Chapter

8

Neurological Reparative Therapy Intervention Protocol in Action — Case Example

In the following case example of a foreign born child adopted into the United States, the emphasis will be on the complexity of the child's problem areas and a detailed description of the Intervention Protocol for Neurological Reparative Therapy.

Jorge

Jorge was born in a small village a day's walk from the large capitol city in Guatemala. He was unfortunate to have been affected by drugs before birth. As a young woman Jorge's mother found the most lucrative employment she could to help support her ill mother and her three siblings. The job that paid the best in a remote area in the hills outside her village was processing cocaine for shipment to Mexico and eventually to the United States. As a teenager at the time, she was also exposed to the use of cocaine by her employer who preferred to pay employees with abundant cocaine rather than cash. At first she resisted, but other workers told her cocaine made the difficult work easier and soon her experimentation led to continual use. A short time later she was paid entirely in the drug. Drug usage is initially a sure route to the pleasure center of the brain which is bathed in dopamine. Once the nucleus accumbens septi (pleasure center) has repeatedly been stimulated by a drug such as cocaine, it begins the process of physical and psychological addiction. Some

165

drugs produce this state of addiction more quickly than others and cocaine is one of the quickest addicting substances known.

Jorge's mother lost sight of why she took the job in the first place and soon was unable to support either herself or her family. The many negative effects of the drug also caused her to be a marginal worker and she lost her job, but not her addiction that had come from the job. Now unemployed, unable to support herself or her family and with an addiction that required a daily influx of cash, this unskilled young woman then turned to the only other job she could find to obtain money for her addiction — prostitution. While working at this job, on a drug high to mask the shame of what she did, she became pregnant with Jorge.

Jorge's mother had no medical care and no experience with a pregnancy, and thus was into her second trimester before she knew she carried a child. All the while her drug-use continued. By this time the developing brain of her child had been significantly influenced by both the drug and the lack of personal care of his mother. Like many addicts, his mother saw nothing more important than the drug — not eating, sleeping or even living. The drug was more important than the idea of a child growing within her. Jorge was born premature, with low birth weight and addicted to cocaine.

Jorge's mother was unable to stop or control her addiction over the years following his birth and this resulted in a host of negative environmental elements including poor nutrition, neglect, and a distant and unresponsive mother who was either high on her drug or working to get her next fix. Jorge's brain adapted to the world it experienced. After frequent periods of placing Jorge with his grandmother, by the age of 18 months Jorge was living with his ailing grandmother full-time with infrequent visits by his mother. His grandmother was not sure whether it was worse that the visits were infrequent or that they happened at all, since both resulted in emotional and behavioral reactivity from little Jorge. As her health worsened, his grandmother approached an international adoption organization and asked for help. She knew her years were numbered and there was no safety net in her country for children unlucky enough to be in Jorge's position.

Jorge was an attractive but deeply troubled child. Too often being physically attractive is a stronger predictor of adoption than the needs of the child. The international adoptive agency had little trouble finding a willing and well-to-do American family.

Alcohol/Drug Related Neurological Disorder

There are many periods of critical brain growth and development but none are more important than the prenatal period. While drugs can harm the developing child's brain, the most harmful drug is alcohol which is toxic and damages neuro-development. Any substance the mother ingests enters the fetus' body and brain and alcohol is legal, cheap and the most available drug of choice. The impacts of this toxin on the developing brain include a wide variety of impairments: nerve damage, central and peripheral nervous system damage, damaged amygdala and hippocampus, cortical atrophy, and gene and neurotransmitter functioning. After birth additional impacts can include: sleep disorder, balance problems, impaired problem-solving, regulation of sensory input, emotional dysregulation, and poor abstract reasoning. Severity of impairment can be from mild to severe. Some children with Fetal Alcohol Syndrome have permanent brain damage, however, most ARND symptoms are showing encouraging signs of improvement with the right treatments over long periods of intervention. The encouraging message is there is hope for many children who are affected by drugs and alcohol.

Jorge was four at the time he entered his new family. To say that his new life was foreign to him was a major understatement. He was in a new country, with a different language, he knew no one and nothing was familiar from the food to the strange habits of his family reaching out and nurturing him. All of this was an extremely difficult adjustment, but his brain was once again prepared to adapt to the hand it was dealt. To symbolize his new world, the family changed not only his last name to theirs, but they changed his first name as well. He was now George and the transformation was all but complete. There was only one problem: George's brain was still the drug-affected, neglected and traumatized brain of little Jorge, and all of the external changes in his world did not change this fact.

George was referred to Jasper Mountain after two and a half years of psychological, educational and psychiatric treatment, none of which worked. During all this time he grew larger and stronger, but not more adjusted to the world around him. He was agitated, angry and violent nearly every day. His most frequent target was his adoptive mother, not just because she spent the most time with him, but also because he seemed to be particularly triggered by her to agitation and aggression. When he became too violent to be maintained at home, he was placed at a specialized center for children with similar backgrounds. In this setting he could be maintained by caregivers agreeing to his constant demands. But he was getting older and larger but not better. His family could see this very clearly.

As is often the case in situations such as this, the family was more devastated than George. The family was left with the broken dreams of a successful adoption, the pain that their love was not wanted by George and clearly was not enough to meet his substantial needs. To add to the pressure, the mounting financial problems had now lowered the family's standard of living.

As something of a last attempt at finding some hope, the family brought seven-year-old George to Jasper Mountain. George was a unique and difficult challenge even for Jasper Mountain. The challenge came from the drug exposure, the serious emotional and behavioral problems, and the non-stop demands that turned into violence if not met exactly as he specified. In fact, George was showing himself to be one of the most difficult of the difficult population in the program. It was clear that the task at hand was to change the way George's brain operated. The way he perceived adults, the way he felt about the world around him and the way he behaved, all had to be changed. This major neurological readjustment would need to start from the inside out.

After months of struggle, the Neurological Reparative Therapy Intervention Protocol was used to develop a comprehensive plan for George. As described in Chapter Six, the protocol has four main steps. The following is how this protocol informed the treatment for George:

Step 1 — Defining the Problem

George had many challenging behavior problems that are frequently found in children with his background. The one unique feature in his case was the severity of most of the problem areas. It is important when addressing a problem to insure that the right problem is identified. It happens all too frequently that parents, teachers and mental health professionals focus on the wrong issue, with the predictable result that working on the wrong problem does little to inform an effective solution.

Problem Areas

George had a range of very unpleasant emotional and behavior issues that were very difficult for his family and very hard on him. These issues included frequent violent tantrums. George not only let everyone around him know when he was not pleased, he would attack adults as well as attempting to harm himself. He did not seem to discriminate whom he tried to hurt, except a mother figure often received the worst treatment. The dynamic of targeting any mother figure was particularly challenging because in most families, the relationship between the mother and child determines to a great extent the mood of the household and the prospects for a successful adoption.

George had other problem areas in addition to his violence. He was often verbally assaultive and frequently made death threats. He was also anxious throughout the day. Any change in his schedule, any surprise events that he was not anticipating, and any situation that might produce some anxiousness in a normal child would result in a moderate to severe emotional and behavioral meltdown. George required the undivided focus of an adult during all waking hours. Such a need for one-on-one supervision at all times put an additional stress on the adoptive family. What made the situation even worse was the fact that even with one-to-one attention during every waking moment, George was getting older, larger and stronger, but George was not getting better.

Target Symptom Statement

The specific focus of our immediate intervention was the following target symptom statement. The complexity of problem areas some children demonstrate can become overwhelming not only to parents but also therapists. It is important to identify a very specific behavior to be the focus of an intervention. After consideration of many problem behaviors, the immediate focus would be the target symptom statement, *George's violent attacks on female care providers multiple times per day when he perceived that he was not in total control*. This target symptom was specific to who, what, when and could be easily measured.

Step 2—Translating the Behavior

A. Finding the meaning of the behavior. Using the concept of translating the behavior to see the meaning to the child, the following were the potential translations of the target symptom.

- I can't count on adults to care for me
- I am angry that my mother neglected me
- I must control every situation to be safe
- My needs are so great they can't be met
- If I am bad enough I will be given what I want
- I will only get what I need if I threaten to hurt people
- I'm a bad person and I hate myself
- I need you but I hate you
- I am possessed by a demon*
- I must find someone who will accept me
- I am an alien here to take over the planet*

*In order to consider a wider range of possible translations, it is often helpful to come up with translations that are way outside the box to encourage broader thinking. The above starred items represent possible meaning to the behavior that would certainly not be typically considered. It is often helpful to have such items to encourage the team considering possible interventions to think more creatively. Too often parents and professionals move too quickly through the steps of the protocol. Encouraging more creative thinking is often useful to come up with more innovative thinking and innovative solutions. As in many cases, the two outlandish starred items held some grain of truth in George's case. His higher order brain functions had been hijacked, not by a demon but by his history that included a toxic foreign substance causing him to feel and act differently than everyone around him. However, if the adverse impacts of his past could be mitigated he would be less "possessed" and could learn to fit into the world around him. Being possessed and feeling like an alien turned out to be useful metaphors for the people helping George.

B. Understanding the most accurate meaning of the child's words using the concept of translating words to understand the meaning to the child, consider if the child speaks in opposites. The following are frequent verbalized statements George made when he was under internal stress. The statements on the right change these statements to an opposite meaning.

"I want to kill you"	I need you
"Don't touch me"	Please comfort me
"I hate you"	I'm feeling too close to you
"You don't care about me"	Your caring is worrying me
"I don't want you around me"	Please don't leave me
"I just want to die"	I have to survive

Step 3 — Determine the Causes of the Problem

The causes of problem behaviors are generally more difficult to determine than in George's case. Many children have missing information about the pregnancy and early years of life. With less than full information there are times that theories or best guesses of the child's past must be used. However, in George's situation the facts were relatively clear. Early drug exposure, neglect and deprivation in the early critical years resulted in an insecure attachment. Although neglect (which has the most pervasive long-term impact of any type of abuse) decreased after his early years, George did not develop a secure attachment in the home placements up to and including his adoptive home. All these problems are known to cause predictable issues with children. In George's case the cause and effect relationship of maltreatment and poor attachment were not hard to see. Finding some answers to address these issues would prove to be a much more daunting challenge.

Step 4 — Develop the Intervention

Taking into consideration the outcome of Step 2, it is important to consider what the most accurate translation of the child's behaviors and words may be. To discern the most accurate message from the child requires both experience and intuition, but is less difficult than it may seem. The translations may ultimately be incorrect, but if so this should become apparent. The following translations were viewed as the most authentic and accurate:

a. The lack of the ability to cope with events was producing a need to control everyone and every situation.

b. The lack of internal belief in self or the ability to be self-reliant.

   c. An insecure attachment was resulting in non-stop demands.

   d. Violent behavior was coming from a fight/flight activation of survival response connected even to minor issues.

   e. George frequently spoke in opposites, so his statements could be reversed to learn what he was really trying to say.

From these endorsed themes, interventions were developed in order to address the target symptom statement:

   a. The constant attempts to control everyone and everything were clearly not helping George cope with daily situations. This placed him in the bind that he was uncomfortable when others made decisions affecting him, but when he fought for control and even when he prevailed, he felt no more security nor any comfort. Therefore the only way that George was going to become less anxious about his life being managed was to learn to rely on adults as all children have to learn.

The intervention would be to hold George accountable to hear and follow the directions of adults. He would not give up his control easily and would become repeatedly violent as if being attacked, but it was essential for him to learn that he must do what adults expected of him. As he followed the directions of adults, his many demands would be met with the adults modifying some aspect of what he wanted. As he did what he was expected to do, he would be allowed to receive some of what he wanted. Over time this would teach George that when the adults are in charge he was free to be less concerned about controlling his life and he could be a child. George had to learn that it is a big job to be concerned with safety and getting all your basic needs met, a job best left to competent adults. He would also need to learn that getting what he wanted was linked with reliance upon the adults in his life.

b. George's lack of belief in himself was addressed by providing reflections from others concerning his skills and abilities. He would need to learn to see himself in the positive ways that others saw him and his abilities, to learn to use his skills to accomplish small successes. In this intervention it was important that the adults not consistently be critical of George or his internal sense of failure would be reinforced.

c. George's insecure attachment would need to be improved and to do so he was provided one check-in person in each situation he was in at home, at school, in team sports, etc. One adult would provide him directions, interact with him, and make decisions for him. With one person to respond to, George would need to learn to rely on one adult to take care of things and to get what he wanted. Because the adult would change, George would learn to rely on a variety of adults in care provider roles, therefore broadening his reliance on others.

d. George's violence was addressed with every aspect of his plan. The premise that George's violence was coming from his perceived lack of safety (thus resulting in the fight/ flight reactive stress response) would be addressed by the combination of the following: an improved attachment, increased reliance on adults, improvements in self-confidence, and by increasing the positive touch he received rather than the aggressive touch of attacking and being contained by adults when he was violent. When George was doing his part in the plan, he was invited to sit on the lap of his check-in staff (usually female) and be rocked, an activity that he both needed and enjoyed.

e. George's frequent speaking in opposites when under stress was addressed by adults ignoring the content of his statements and instead responding to the translated meaning. This process would reflect to George that the adults around him understood what he was thinking and feeling, and over time he could more accurately reflect his experience.

Step 5 — Evaluating the Result

It is often true that children who have emotional or behavioral disturbances give up too early on challenging tasks. It is also true that adults often do the same. Step 5 is an attempt to counter the tendency to try an intervention and if it fails try it again, and after the third failure give up and consider the problem too difficult to solve. Step 5 focuses on evaluating the effectiveness of interventions in order to first see if the plan is working, but also to give the message that in nearly every case there will be changes and adjustments along the way. In other words, expect some failure in interventions and always be prepared to make adjustments without getting discouraged or frustrated. In the evaluation process the interventions are not expected to work perfectly and alterations are expected.

In George's case the team of individuals working with George's family all seemed to get new energy when George began to change in a positive way. This often happens as soon as a new plan is developed. However, everyone can get discouraged if they do not trust that an intervention has much hope of success. After a few days, George began to feel more attention from the adults at home and at school and it was a different type of attention that he liked but was not used to — positive attention. He had a check-in person who he went to with his numerous worries and demands. Because he worked with one adult in each situation, he received a more consistent response which helped him to feel more secure since the response was more predictable. Within 60 days the target symptom behavior was reduced substantially (more than a 50% reduction in violence toward female care providers).

Just because the overall interventions were showing success did not mean that we were over the hill and only needed to coast. George had a number of serious issues and as one issue improved, it was important to move to the next problem and go through the process once again. If this seems like a great deal of work, it most assuredly is a great deal of work to gradually improve the serious problem areas of a difficult child.

What was this approach designed to do?

George both needed the help of adults and at the same time he did not trust anyone to really provide him what he needed and wanted. With this combination of interventions, George was forced to rely on adults and in the process began to learn that some adults really could provide him with the consistency and attention he so desperately wanted and needed. Improving the confidence in others repaired some of the damaged attachment of his early years. Improved attachment with trusted adults also gradually repaired some of the impacts of his alcohol-related neurological disorder. Just as negative issues in his early years (poor attachment, drug poisoning, neglect) worked against his developing brain, now positive repair components (improved attachment, increased emotional regulation, reduced stress) worked together synergistically to become more than the positive sum of the parts. Learning to rely on adults helped him because he could not rely on himself due to his lack of self-confidence. His dependence and interdependence improved and the requirement that he give to others to obtain what he wanted from them (other than basic needs) helped him learn reciprocity. Each of these improvements developed a growing sense of attachment to the primary adults around George. While George improved, his issues remained and the neurological changes needed time to become stronger than his old habitual patterns. There were no quick or easy answers to George, or any child with significant neurological impairments. George's future is beginning to look much brighter for the first time, but much work is left to be done. Improvement is a long road and a difficult journey to be taken one step at a time.

NRT Intervention Protocol

Step 1—Define the correct problem.

Step 2—Translate the meaning of the behavior then translate the verbal messages.

Step 3—Take the time to consider the causes of the problem.

Step 4—Identify very specific interventions to address the deeper issues of the problem.

Step 5—Evaluate the results and be prepared to make adjustments to every intervention.

The primary weakness of interventions for complex problems in children is addressing the symptoms rather than the deeper issues of the problem.

Take the time to look a little deeper and avoid the tendency to rush to find a quick answer.

Chapter

9

Understanding the Real Problem can Lead to
Counterintuitive Interventions — Case Example

In this case example the emphasis will be on the counterintuitive nature of the treatment approach when attempts using traditional approaches consistently failed.

Cal was named after the great state where he was born. However in every state and in every town there are shadowy areas where people live in the margins of society and do their best just to get by. Cal was from a rural area where the main economy was not the logging industry, as presented in the Chamber of Commerce literature, but was the cash crop marijuana. The primary pastime of this part of California was not the All-American game of baseball, but the more frequently indulged activity of heavy drinking in one of the taverns that outnumbered the local churches 5 to 1.

Cal's mother grew up in the area and dropped out of school at age fifteen when it just seemed right to do so since she could get a job waiting tables. A job of her own implied independence and less trouble buying the cigarettes she began using at age eleven with her friends. Cal's mother was assaulted and raped one night in a car in the restaurant parking lot after closing by a customer that she smiled at while serving his dinner. She told no one and this is when cigarettes were not enough to handle the pain and she began helping herself to the alcohol that was available at work. Three years and several jobs later she found herself pregnant, on her own with two and a half addictions – tobacco, alcohol and the increasingly occurring use of methamphetamines. She did not realize she was pregnant until two months later and by then was not sure who the sperm donor had been. Of the three possible men, none were characters she wanted to ever see again, much less share raising a child. So she decided to have the child on her own, and at this point did her best to reduce her reliance on her addictive substances and only drank on weekends but could not give up the cigarettes. Her smokes were the one stress release she allowed herself despite being pregnant.

Cal was born a month premature with low birth weight and a disposition characterized by irritability and fussiness. This disposition would only grow worse over the next six years.

Cal was referred for help by his school district when he demonstrated excessive issues throughout his kindergarten year and now in first grade he was unmanageable. Cal was intellectually bright and perhaps a bit too smart in his ability to manipulate his mother and most adults he interacted with. He seemed to know what adults wanted and would gain the upper hand by being one step ahead of them and he was not willing to give any adult whatever they wanted. This was oppositional defiant behavior as an Olympic sport, and Cal could make the Olympic team.

We obtained detailed information from his mother and learned not only of his early years but of the multiple failed relationships she had that resulted in a home life too often characterized by alcohol abuse, neglect, and domestic violence. Cal's mother felt she had always had bad luck in her relationships with men because they consistently used and abuse her. She could not see her responsibility in the choices she made along the way. She did feel bad about the violence Cal had been exposed to and she knew this did not help his angry and reactive disposition. She also hoped that her frequent use of alcohol and methamphetamines early in the pregnancy were not contributing factors, but her tears of guilt indicated she knew they probably were. She emphatically disagreed with the research that tobacco was bad for developing fetuses.

Of the many negative factors in Cal's environment, one controlling, bullying, abusive live-in partner of his mom's stood out. In the six-month torrid relationship, she had been beaten severely twice and punched, roughed up, and choked multiple times until an abuse shelter helped her relocate. During this period Cal not only observed abuse but was the target on numerous occasions due to his irritable and oppositional nature. This abusive man handled not getting his every wish with violence and Cal gave no adults what they wanted.

With the referral, the school district asked for help in finding a way to get through to Cal. They believed he was intelligent but his non-stop refusals to comply with any direction from a teacher, along with his verbal and physical aggression, made him unworkable in a public school setting and he was only six years old.

The Target Symptom Statement

The extreme level of Cal's oppositionality is difficult to describe. The resulting problems working with him, much less parenting him, were considerable. He was referred to and admitted into a school designed for children with past issues similar to his. After attempting many of the interventions that work with other difficult children, it was clear Cal would take special attention. We had to work with a focus on one behavior at a time while doing our best with his many other problem areas. A team meeting resulted in the identification of the following target symptom statement— frequent physical aggression toward female school staff when he was given a direction of any kind. Now in the first grade, Cal spent most of the school day outside of the classroom because of his screaming tantrums and physical aggression toward his teacher and the aides who worked with him.

Translating the Meaning of the Problem

It is pertinent to mention that even in a program that has consistent success with the most difficult children, Cal so far was the exception—nothing seemed to work. This resulted in predictable patterns among the staff who worked with him. They requested that he be removed from the program because he was not improving (we do not remove any child because of difficult behavior). The teacher and aides were abused, exhausted, more than a little angry at Cal, and had little or no confidence the situation could be improved. The team met to develop an intervention protocol based upon Neurological Reparative Therapy.

The team considered over twenty possible translations of Cal's behaviors. They included:

- I hate myself
- I hate my mother (he targeted females)
- I want to be in charge
- Get out of my way or I will hurt you
- I am a frightened animal who snarls and bites when afraid
- I want as much negative attention as I can get

- I want to hurt you like I was hurt
- I don't like school
- I am possessed by a demon*
- I have PTSD flashbacks when adults give me directions and I fight back
- I have a violent disposition due to my genetics*
- I enjoy making adults look like incompetent fools
- I don't know how to get along with anyone
- I am alone, scared and unhappy
- Please rescue me from the prison I am in
- I have to be the most aggressive person in the room to prevail
- If I am hurtful enough, the adults will give up and leave me alone
- I hurt the people I care about*
- I lose at everything except being the best at being the worst
- I cannot find any place where the adults are strong enough to keep me safe

The * items indicate the encouraged attempts to think broadly, outside of the box and even a bit bizarre; this can help adults get beyond their preconceived ideas.

As the team went through this process, the hopelessness in the staff who worked with Cal every day seemed to change. This often happens when adults want to help a child but don't understand how to do so. No one likes to fail, then redouble their efforts to fail more spectacularly. In Cal's case the first step was to understand the inner world of the child because only when we know the problem do we have a good chance at determining the solution.

We went through the list and endorsed the following as the primary translations of Cal's violent behavior toward females:

- I am a frightened animal who snarls and bites when afraid
- I hurt the people I care about*
- I am alone, scared and unhappy
- I have to be the most aggressive person in the room to prevail

With these items being the most likely translation, the team began to see a different picture emerging. Yes, Cal was an extremely unpleasant child to interact with and all your efforts were met not only with resistance but with aggression, however, what was behind this pattern was a scared child being protected by a snarling watchdog inside of him. The staff began to see that his hurtful behavior may, in fact, come from his liking the person he hurts rather than hating them. Finally, it seemed that Cal was pleading with staff to show him that they were strong enough to protect him by being powerful and non-aggressive—a combination Cal had not experienced in his life from adults.

The second part of the translating step was to review his verbal statements when he was feeling stressed (most of the time). To do this the team was asked to write down what Cal typically verbalized. Here are some of Cal's typical statements on the left and a reframed opposite statement on the right to see which was closer to being accurate:

"Get away from me"   Don't leave me

"I don't want to learn"   Help me to learn

"I hate this place"	I need this place
"You just want to hurt me"	Please don't hurt me
"I like to hurt people"	I don't like to hurt people
"I want to be left alone"	Please don't let me be alone
"You are a fucking idiot"	Be smart enough to help me
"I want it my way"	I need strong adults to be safe

Gill's Struggles With His Relationship With His Mother

Gill came across as an angry and anxious child when he entered Jasper Mountain. He constantly attacked female treatment team members with aggression and violence, especially the ones that he subconsciously considered to be mother figures. This pattern became even more pronounced when he moved to a practice family setting. In individual therapy, he had to learn to express his genuine feelings about his relationship with his mother and understand the connection between his past relationship with his mother and his present relationships with females. Gill needed to express his ambivalent relationship with his mother and his need to be loyal and protective of his family in a safe and nurturing environment. Gill slowly learned that he was not angry at a new mother figure in his life, but actually he was sad about his biological mother and what he did not get from her. Then he was able to move to the next level of his treatment. There was nothing easy in Gill's journey but every successful connection with a supportive adult reduced his depression. Gill may always struggle with trusting others particularly those he cares about, but he started his journey of recovery at an early age and he has a good chance at a good life ahead.

Femeke Britschgi Cabernard, Ph.D.

Similar to many children with traumatic and chaotic pasts, Cal spoke in opposites when he was under stress. Despite the fact that most of his team had felt his verbal and physical wrath and had been physically assaulted by him on many occasions, the team said that each of the statements on the right were more true for Cal than those on the left. The team began to see that Cal was a frightened child desperately and frantically calling attention to himself, wanting strong adults to demonstrate to him that they could help keep him safe. This was an entirely different perspective of the target symptom of verbal and physical aggression toward adults, particularly toward females.

In this case three translations were added in the outside the box category. The first was that Cal was possessed by a demon, the second was a problem with his genetics and finally he hurt those he loved. Cal was not possessed by a demon other than his past. However, it appeared that his genetics did play some role in his behavior. Finally, it was quite clear that he did hurt the ones he cared for. As in other cases, the unlikely translations ended up having more than a little truth and adding to the treatment plan.

Causes of the Problem

The next step in the intervention protocol was considering the causes of the problem and answering the question of what would produce his affective disposition and his serious behaviors. For this step the team reviewed Cal's history. Could he have been impaired by his mother's use of substances? This can result in an over-activated central nervous system producing anxiety and irritability. Cal did not have Fetal Alcohol Syndrome but he could be on the continuum of Alcohol Related Neurological Disorder. Other potential contributing causes could be Cal's focus on females, either wanting to retaliate or desperately needing a mother figure to be strong and protective in the face of aggression. The exposure to domestic violence and his own abuse would also likely be factors in Cal's propensity to aggression.

When the team took the time to review the details of his short life's experience, there was a much better understanding that Cal's present was being linked in his mental perceptual system as an extension of his past. He experienced that he was still in a hostile, chaotic and unsafe environment without being able to see that he was the source of most of this pattern continuing in his life. More precisely, his traumatic memories were replicating his past and bringing it into the present until he perceived something different. From this review the team formed the premise that Cal was a hurt and frightened child who had watched the aggressor and abuser being the only one in the environment who was safe. This was the pattern that he was replicating. However, underneath this pattern was the child who was frantically crying for help because he knew that he could not possibly keep himself safe despite his most aggressive and crafty attempts to do so.

Interventions

Over the course of Cal's treatment, dozens of interventions were developed and specifically based upon the above process. Two of the many resulting interventions will be described. With the help of this intervention protocol, Cal's team was seeing from a new perspective most everything Cal was doing, along with the entire dynamics in the classroom. They could see that much of what they had been doing with Cal was counter-productive. They were too quick to listen to his words and believe he did not respect female staff or have any interest in them. They viewed his efforts to resist learning in a new way, as well as his words and behaviors that before seemed to be attempts to push people away rather than a deep desire to be close and comforted by a protective adult. The team could see that Cal had not responded to many of the interventions that work with other children because they were designing the interventions for the wrong child, the child he attempted to present rather than who he was on the inside. Now the team was ready to consider interventions that had a chance at success.

We started with the issue that seemed to be the most important translation—the aggressor was the only one who was safe in the environment. What this implied was that Cal could use some help in effective ways to find safety because being physically aggressive did not result in him experiencing any safety. We picked a male staff who Cal perceived as powerful, and Cal received direct lessons in how to learn real power rather than pseudo power. His considerable intellectual curiosity was targeted and he was taught how to control himself, how to learn to relax and control his anxiety. He was given models of power figures and what made them powerful. He was helped to understand some of the aspects of martial arts and the internal confidence to face conflict. Cal was young but very intelligent and responded very well to these lessons. Rather than math and reading, here was a lesson that his brain knew was useful.

The point needs to be made here that such an intervention would have created strong resistance among the team if the intervention protocol process had not been followed. Why would you teach a power hungry child how to be more powerful? Who would foolishly teach an aggressive child components of martial arts? However, these counterintuitive approaches made sense to the team once the deeper issues were considered.

While Cal was receiving an education in being a more genuinely powerful person, we still needed to address the classroom and his disruptiveness. To do this it was acknowledged that all the academic testing done with Cal identified that despite the fact that he was in the classroom approximately 33% of the day, he was at grade level in all subjects. In other words, Cal was bright enough to be picking up information in his own way and was not missing out on learning just because he spent much of his day tantruming and refusing to comply with educational expectations. With the knowledge that Cal was learning, just not the way we expected him to do so, we had the space to be able to try other counterintuitive interventions. Because Cal spoke in opposites, we decided to have a chess move of our own. Instead of having Cal start his day in the classroom, he was told that there would be little to nothing that we thought he would be interested in, so he was given an area in the school but out of the classroom where he was not expected to do anything in particular. He could read books of his choice, and one of the staff brought in an old and very primitive (boring) hand-held video game. Our goal was to counter his oppositionality and refusals by turning the tables and expecting little of him to give him little to oppose.

When this phase of his plan was implemented he was at first caught off guard, he did not expect to have school staff tell him that nothing was being taught that would interest him. For a day or two he took a nap, looked at books and played the video game, but seemed to be wondering what was going on in the class. It was more fun to be in the class and finding ways to get removed, with all the accompanying attention, than it was to be out of the class and wondering what all the other children were getting to do. Cal was not banned from the classroom, we just told him he had told us enough times that he was not interested in staying in the class and learning and we now believed him and he did not have to be in class.

Cal was smart enough to get a bit suspicious at what was going on. If our plan was to have him out of the classroom, he decided to oppose the plan and wanted into the classroom. He was allowed to return if he followed the rules. Of course, once back in the classroom he tried to return to the old pattern of being disruptive and limits were set that if he did this twice, he would be allowed to receive the lessons but not in the classroom. Over the next few weeks he started each day doing nothing, but was bored quickly and asked for assignments. Over time he asked to return to the classroom with the other children and we had him earn the privilege. Not only did this disrupt the negative pattern between Cal and the school staff, but it also reestablished the control of the classroom back into the hands of the staff which reenergized them to work with Cal with new energy and commitment. Week after week, Cal asked for more and more school work and slowly he earned getting back into the classroom, but it was his desire, not because it was the staff requirement.

Did the Intervention Work?

The original target symptom statement was Cal's verbal and physical aggression primarily to female staff in the school when given a direction. He had many other problem issues and the interventions went far beyond the two mentioned above (teaching him power and not having him in the classroom). The immediate result of the team's work was that the tone of the school completely changed in relationship to Cal. The staff were back in charge of the decisions and tone of the classroom and Cal was experiencing strong adults who were doing what he really wanted them to do which was to keep him safe. And what about the main problem of aggression? Over the months following the implementation of this plan, Cal's aggression was reduced by 95%! If any member of the team had initially suggested that this power hungry child be taught to be more powerful, or had suggested to give this child who did not want to be in the classroom the choice to not be in class, such suggestions would have been met with confusion or ridicule. However, it was the team that came up with these and other counterintuitive interventions that actually worked.

With such an improvement in the target symptom, was this a miraculous cure? Not at all, Cal continued to test in a variety of ways. For example, once school was more firmly in the hands of adults, he escalated problem issues at home. When he figured out what adults wanted, he would revert to finding a way to disrupt their efforts. The fact that he was less aggressive was only a start, a good start, but there would be much more to do. Cal improved significantly in his initial classroom and graduated to a new school where he started off being in class the majority of time. The gradual process continued of developing new neurotemplates such as perceiving adults as safe because they were strong and capable. Behavioral changes can occur quickly with a well-placed intervention, but deeper changes take time because the brain must change and most positive brain changes require mastery coming from repetition. Cal's future success was in no way guaranteed by the process described above, he and the adults around him would have much more work to do. He is an example of many challenging children in that as soon as one behavior improves, another problem behavior surfaces. There are no easy ways to do a very difficult task, and parenting and treating children similar to Cal is a very difficult task indeed. This case was offered here to reflect how understanding the real problem is critical to a successful intervention, and at times what works may be the last thing you might expect. Deeper understanding of a child's brain and perceptual system may at times lead to counterintuitive interventions that address not what is on the surface but at deeper levels of meaning to the child and, more importantly, to the child's brain.

Understanding the Real Problem and Counterintuitive Interventions

When working with difficult children, the shortest distance between two points may not be a straight line.

The real problem is often below the surface and very different than what it may appear.

Thinking outside usual solutions is encouraged and often very helpful for developing interventions.

It is typical for children with emotional disturbances to say the opposite of what they mean.

Interventions do not work unless they address the right problem, not just the symptoms.

Counterintuitive interventions may seem precisely what you don't want to do, which is often why they work.

If an intervention repeatedly fails, try something else or it is the adult who is demonstrating poor thinking.

Chapter

10

The Jasper Mountain Story — Innovation Coming from Direct Experience

To the degree that Neurological Reparative Therapy has some value to guide individuals to a better life, it may be of interest to learn more about the environment that synthesized this approach — Jasper Mountain. This unique facility is not in Wyoming, as some people assume, that would be Casper. It is also not Jasper National Park, that would be in Canada. Jasper Mountain is in the beautiful foothills of the Cascade Mountains east of Springfield/ Eugene, Oregon. Like many other aspects of the Jasper Mountain program, the environment was carefully selected by the people who started the organization.

The Founders

The beginnings of Jasper Mountain go back to the deserts of Arizona where the founders first were involved in helping children and looking for better and more effective answers and solutions. Of the three founders, one worked in a medical research organization, among other roles, as a biofeedback therapist. The 1970s was an exciting time for innovation and some of the early work was focused on how the body could heal itself. Biofeedback was one of the areas of medical research that was showing that long-held views of "involuntary" systems within the human body were, in fact, accessible to voluntary control. So one of the founders had spent a decade being exposed to cutting edge medical research that questioned many of the beliefs about how the body and the human brain worked.

The second founder had a combination of interests that also played a role in founding Jasper Mountain. With a background in administration and working in a youth-serving agency, it was the growing recognition that children were being mistreated and traumatized in shocking numbers that primarily caught her interest. There is a belief that our society and the medical field have always worked to prevent and treat child abuse, but this assumption is far from accurate. It was not until Drs. C. Henry Kempe and Brandt Steele coined the term "battered child syndrome" in the 1960s that the medical field began to see that the cause of many physical issues coming into clinics and hospitals were the result of maltreatment by adults. Even then it was not until the 1970s that programs began to focus on helping the victims of abuse. The recognition of the epidemic of child abuse came even later due to the collective denial and refusal to believe that adults, especially parents, would seriously harm children, at times, in intentional and sadistic ways. During this time it was the plight of these early abuse victims that caught the interest and commitment of one of Jasper Mountain's founders.

The third founder was a mental health professional who went through graduate school in child and family therapy in the early part of the 1970s. This was a time of upheaval in society that spawned innovation in education and a time of significant self-reflection. It seemed that every aspect of society was being questioned from politics, medical science, psychology, religion, sexual mores, gender equality and how children were being treated. In this environment of questioning everything, new answers and solutions were being posed and tested in many areas of society. For example, the 1970s was the greenhouse where many of today's most innovative organizations had their roots, and this includes Jasper Mountain. The third founder was interested in the emerging knowledge of effective psychological treatment, the impact of systems and environments, and how meditation and spiritual mindfulness promoted optimal health. As a child and family therapist, he noticed a dynamic that outpatient family therapy was very effective for 85 to 90 percent of children. However, there was a growing awareness that problems in adolescence and adulthood often had their causes going back to early childhood. It was a time of early recognition of what the human brain was capable of but with little ability to know how or why. In this context, the third founder was committed to implementing new approaches to optimum health while pursuing a life of service to others.

Early Conceptualization of a Village

Two of the founders married in 1972. They met the third founder through a network of individuals who were questioning traditional assumptions of society and its institutions and over time developed an intentional community based upon shared values, optimum health and service to others. Two of the founders also worked in a branch of a national initiative of federally sponsored youth-serving organizations that were funded to understand, prevent and treat problems of children and adolescents.

An outgrowth of the intentional community developed by the founders was a series of discussions of like-minded individuals who also wished to question old assumptions and make a difference in helping others. Many of the themes in this environment led to a group commitment to values such as personal health, environmental consciousness, service to others, and investment in the family, specifically to children. These values emerged from weekly discussions/debates and over several years led to a plan to operationalize a lifestyle that would include the above values.

Why Oregon?

At the time plans were being discussed of creating an intentional village where shared values could be supported by those involved, the founders were very involved in their work at the medical research clinic and the youth-serving organization. However, it became increasingly clear that the Phoenix area, although beautiful most of the year, was headed in the direction of a mega-city complete with all the accompanying problems — congestion, crowding, environmental pollution, personal stress, human isolation and the rapid dissolution of the extended family that was the basis of support for individuals for hundreds and even thousands of years.

It also became clear that a significant amount of time was being spent in activities that were not conducive to optimal health. For example, members spent more time commuting in stop and go freeway traffic each day than talking to each other. Dinners on the run and hours in front of the television were a few of many societal practices that were not endorsed by the new family. As the many components of optimal health were discussed and added to the list, it became progressively clear that significant lifestyle changes would be needed to follow the vision of a village where health of mind, body and spirit would be promoted and modeled to the children. A major question was where all this could take shape and a mega-city was not optimal.

The search for an ideal place initially was a data-driven project. The group identified the measures to determine a healthy place

—a quality environment with clean air and water, open natural spaces, minimal exposure to natural disasters such as violent weather, diversity of people and acceptance of a broad range of perspectives, a stable economy, proximity to a larger community, a location with natural beauty, among a long list of indicators of a desirable location. From this list data helped narrow the search to three areas of the Country—northernmost California, southwestern Colorado and southern Oregon. Visits were made to each area and Oregon became the choice. We were not the only ones choosing this area of Oregon. During our search, Eugene, Oregon was named the nation's most livable midsized city and Portland, Oregon was named the nation's most livable large city. It would be another two years after the selection before moving day. A date was set in the future and when the day arrived, the three founders and two of their children headed for Oregon.

We are often asked how Jasper Mountain came to be, and the above is a more detailed answer than I have even given. I have done so to show the convergence of factors than came together to produce the product that is Jasper Mountain. The background of the founders is important as well as a time in society where new problems were coming to light and old solutions were being questioned. Looking back, there were many roads that converged into what Jasper Mountain has become: a place of innovation and testing new ideas, a deep commitment to living a meaningful life and modeling this to children, and developing the village where adults and children can learn together and grow in self-understanding and personal contentment.

It is important to say that at no time have the founders felt any particular personal responsibility for what has developed over time or felt a sense of satisfaction or major accomplishment. The reason for this is that we have all been too busy keeping the ship afloat to stop and admire how far the organization has come. We also do not take any of the successes personally because we have always been aware that the village is much bigger than any one, or for that matter, three members of the village. A major aspect of Jasper Mountain and a factor in every list of a successful life is a sense of feeling a part of something greater than the self. When this element is an aspect of an organization, then everyone involved has an opportunity to grow in optimal ways. At Jasper Mountain this includes the children, their families, the staff, the Board of Directors, supporters, and everyone connected or even visiting the literal and conceptual village that has organically grown over the last three decades.

Day One

The hard work started long before the first day, but the first child arrived on November 2nd of 1982. After years of talk, planning and visualizing what the ideal environment would be, at some point you have to jump into the water to test your theories and learn to swim. We had suggested to the local child welfare division that we wanted their most difficult children, and we did not have to ask twice since they were happy to oblige. These experienced professionals from sunny Arizona were actually asking for very difficult children to work with and either they were a bubble off center or they were a potential answer to a serious problem. The child welfare staff responded quickly, hoping we were the latter.

The first child was brought to the 'ready for business' program by his caseworker. In the years ahead I was never sure if this child was intended to be a test, but he remains one of the most challenging children we have ever worked with. The child had a list that would become familiar: aggressive, no boundaries, explosive, demanding, hyperactive, poor self-control, reactive, impulsive and a list that could fill the rest of this page. By the end of the first day, we all realized we were now in the deep end of the pool and it was time to sink or swim. There have been many days since then that have been high points and more than a few days where the bottom of the pool was looking pretty familiar. I sincerely mean it when I say it is very difficult to find the space and time to step back and look at successes and how far we have come, because every success brings a larger and more complex challenge to overcome. If someone wished for a full and rewarding lifestyle, here it was and the days, weeks and years have flown by at an amazing speed.

Growth Over Time

From the beginning Jasper Mountain was all about understanding and helping one child at a time. We did our best to understand every child as if they were our own and for a time they were. We also worked hard to understand, support and help the families connected with the children. We often found that due to abuse, neglect and the chaos of their early years, the children learned coping styles that were very damaging to others. At times the families were suffering more than the children were.

Soon after starting the program at Jasper Mountain, efforts began to involve the local community in a concentrated effort to prevent, identify and treat child abuse. Fifteen community leaders were invited to come to an informational discussion about the safety of children in Springfield, Oregon. Fourteen of the fifteen invitees attended. This is noteworthy in itself, but even more impressive was the list of invitees—a legislator, the police chief, the school superintendent, business professionals, city manager, city counselor, and community leaders who could take some type of action if they chose to do so. After one meeting, the group chose to take steps to reduce the amount of child abuse in the area and a program called Springfield Child Abuse Resources was formed. Four years later in 1987, this program merged formally with Jasper Mountain. I say formally because one of the Jasper Mountain founders directed this project and there was informal coordination from day one. Springfield Child Abuse Resources, (SCAR) developed mental health treatment, advocacy and education, special projects, groups for abuse victims and a regional symposium on broad topics related to child abuse.

Continuity among the key people involved in the organization has been a key factor over the years. The founders are still very involved, Board members have impressive longevity with ten, fifteen and twenty years of service. The former city counselor who helped start SCAR is still on staff, and key staff positions within the organization seldom have turnover. There has always been something that has attracted the interest of people to help and stay involved.

Innovation has been another component both in the SCAR program as well as the work going on at Jasper Mountain. Both programs were destined to grow, merge and continue to grow further. In 1989 Jasper Mountain School started to provide an onsite specialized school on the Jasper Mountain campus.

By 1995 a Therapeutic Foster Care Program was started as a step-up and step-down continuum of care for the more damaged children. Children lived with families who were trained and supported by Jasper Mountain staff. Also in 1995, the organization was asked to start a short-term residential evaluation program for children. The new program was housed on 23-acres of rural property a short twenty-minute drive from Jasper Mountain. Children came to the Stabilization, Assessment and Family

Evaluation (SAFE) Center for lengths of stay from 3 to 90 days. The goal of the evaluation was to identify the psychological, educational and practical needs of each child and facilitated the child moving to the appropriate next resource. The condition of the organization to start the program was to have a partnership with the local mental health authority and with the child welfare division, a partnership that is strong to this day.

A Day Treatment Program began in 1997 to accept children from the community who were able to remain in their family home but needed intensive mental health treatment each school day. Children were admitted into the program from local school districts and there were two sites, at Jasper Mountain and at the SAFE Center. Services to the community expanded in 2004 with a wraparound program called the Village Program. Children could remain in their homes and receive intensive support through visiting therapists, skill trainers, mentors and other community supports. The families outlined what they needed to provide their children with an optimal environment for success, building on child and family strengths.

A year later in 2005, the Crisis Response Program began as a partnership between three local social service agencies funded by the local mental health organization. The program became a national model with a hot line, mobile response to the family home, and crisis respite in both facilities and in respite homes. These services were 24/7 for any child age 18 or younger anywhere in the local county which is the size of the State of Connecticut. If a family experienced a problem with a child, help was a phone call away. If a crisis team was needed (about 40% of the time), they arrived at the home in short order. If the situation could not be adequately stabilized, the child could be placed in a respite placement for up to three days. All of the services were provided at no cost to consumers.

As each of these programs developed and grew, so did the overall organization. The number of staff grew from the initial three to the present 130. The budget grew from the initial $30,000 to the present $6,000,000. From humble physical facilities in the early years, we now have architecturally designed facilities that support the important work we do with the children. The organization has three sites with some of the best facilities of any program for children in the world. We owe this to a community that has cared from the beginning and made important things happen for abused and deserving children. From the initial home in 1982, the organization operates the full array of programs we have today. We know the organization is unique in approach, in service integration, in vision and in the practice of taking the most challenging children. The initial home that started in 1982 today is a psychiatric residential treatment center and has the distinction of never in its history rejecting a child or discharging a child due to difficult behavior. Early on and continuing today, the program and staff embrace the challenge of working with the most difficult children because they are our best teachers.

We are often asked how we were able to develop such a comprehensive continuum of mental health services for children. Our answer is that we had to. We did not have other organizations to refer children to and when a need came up we developed the needed service to add to the organization's continuum of care. We did not initially plan to develop a school, a crisis center, a wraparound program, but necessity was the mother of intervention. While developing multiple programs initially created a host of challenges in juggling so many components within one organization, the positive result has been an available

Photo Descriptions

Photo descriptions begin with the top-left photo and continue clockwise.

Page 205 ♦ *Picture of the Jasper Mountain property in 1982.* ♦ *Judy Littlebury — one of the founders at a Halloween party in 1983.* ♦ *An early sign on the highway that has been recently reinstalled.* ♦ *Joyce Ziegler — another founder, proud of the Jasper garden in 1984.* ♦ *The circa 1890s original ranch house was home to the children until 1991.* ♦ *Judy in the barn with a newborn goat.* ♦ *One of many rainbows on the ranch in 1982.*

Page 206 ♦ *Beautiful sunset from the deck of the new Children's Castle in 1992.* ♦ *Part of the extensive temperate rain forest on the property.* ♦ *A child caring for the llamas.* ♦ *A child feeding the horses.* ♦ *A unique Northwest flower, the Fawn Lily (Erythronium Oregonum), growing at Jasper Mountain.* ♦ *Stalls in the new 'Horse Hilton' known as the Jasper Equestrian Center.*

Page 207 ♦ *It is all smiles for one of the Jasper family.* ♦ *The author (far left) white water rafting with the children.* ♦ *Joyce Ziegler with one of the children on the annual mountain camping trip.* ♦ *Children setting a new distance record on the Jasper track.* ♦ *A child competing in the annual Jasper Olympics.* ♦ *Children enjoying the annual trip to high mountain Waldo Lake known to be one of the clearest lakes in the world.* ♦ *A child involved in hands-on learning at Jasper Mountain School.*

Page 208 ♦ *The Children's Castle where twenty of the children reside — in the foreground, the program's llamas out for a walk.* ♦ *The entrance to Jasper Mountain School.* ♦ *Inside the great room of the Children's Castle.* ♦ *The SAFE Center residence and school.* ♦ *The playground and Recreation Building at Jasper.* ♦ *The Recreation Building at the SAFE Center.*

service to match the mental health needs of nearly any child referred to us over the last two decades. Some organizations on principle do not refer to others for a variety of reasons, most related to a belief in a particular approach or model. This is not the case for Jasper Mountain. The only time we would not refer to an available service outside our network of programs would be a bad match between the service and the specific child. There are so many children and families that need help and we have always known that we are a very small part of the overall system of care.

Making a Difference can be Controversial

The road the organization has traveled has never been easy, but some of the challenges have been surprising. For years the goal was to successfully make a difference in the lives of children. What was not anticipated was the more successful the organization became, the more adversaries it developed. Examples of this dynamic are too numerous to present here but a few examples will be offered. The pattern of standing up to controversy emerged very early on with the first major event.

In the early 1980s society was just beginning to realize that children were at risk everywhere in our society. One of the last realizations to occur was the level of sexual abuse in the American culture. The first major event that the organization planned was a theatrically produced stage show to thousands of elementary children on how to spot unwanted touch and learning to be safe. We realized that nowhere in American society do we ever gather thousands of elementary children for anything. Plans for the stage show went well with actors and skits, school districts signed on and the date for the event was set. The largest single event ever held for young children in the United States was approaching when an unlikely adversary emerged — the State child protective services department, Children's Services Division. We were told by this State Department that the event was not to be held. School districts were contacted by the State and told they were not to participate. Pressure was applied in multiple ways. How could the organization responsible for keeping children safe oppose efforts to promote the safety of children? There was one answer, the Division thought the program would be too successful and they could not handle the result of so many children reporting sexual abuse all at once. Amazed by such resistance to reaching out to children living with abuse, the Board of Directors went forward and the event was held. The best efforts of the system to stop the organization's very first event did manage to reduce the numbers of children attending down to a few thousand, but this early experience pointed out a theme that has continued from the beginning of finding unanticipated adversaries to helping children and families.

The next major adversary to our organization helping children came from another institution charged with preparing children for a successful future — the local school district. At an early Board of Directors meeting when plans were approved to expand the number of children in the program, one of the Board members announced he would need to resign due to a conflict of interest. The Board member was the local school district's Director of Special Education. The Board was confused how helping more children could be a conflict of interest but this question was soon clarified. The public school district filed legal appeals in an attempt to close the doors of the organization. Lawyers for the district found every possible means to attack the organization. The reason — Jasper Mountain could become a magnet for children who would be difficult for the district to educate. In legal battles that lasted four years and ended in the State Supreme Court, Jasper Mountain prevailed in ten formal decisions.

We Planted Seeds for the Future

When you plant seeds you can never be sure which ones will sprout and when they will bear fruit. This is particularly true with children. Lynne was a mixed race child with a serious chip on her shoulder. You always knew where you stood with Lynne, and it was seldom a positive place. She was waiting for the next adult to tell her no, and eight years of rage from her abusive past would be focused like a laser beam on sensitive parts of that adult's body. Lynne was a wildcat and staff made sure her claws were trimmed often or their arms would show the result. It is fair to say that during her difficult treatment she improved behaviorally but was never pleasant to be around. She was a child that required paid care takers who switched every eight hours. She might have been the poster child to counter the belief that there is a family for every child. Although she improved in the program, she left the program without gratitude or even much interest in saying goodbye. At Jasper Mountain we view our work with such children as planting seeds for the future. Somewhat to our surprise, Lynne wrote us a letter six years after leaving and she asked me to read it to the current residents. Her letter was filled with positive memories, emotions that were never shared when she was with us about all the good times she had. She pleaded for the children not to be like she was and learn and enjoy Jasper Mountain while they could. She sent us a picture and said she would never forget what we did for her. In Lynne's case the seeds took awhile, but they sprouted and in a somewhat rare occasion we even were able to taste the fruit of our efforts.

Another surprising adversary turned out to be other non-profits whose own missions were similar to Jasper Mountain's in promoting the best interests of children and families. Over time we realized that being a successful non-profit did not always develop support and partnerships with other social service agencies, although at times this did happen. Success was often seen as competition and a threat. Jasper Mountain has frequently been the target of rumors and untrue allegations designed to hurt the organization. None of these attempts have been successful for any period of time.

Over three decades controversy has arisen over Jasper Mountain's beliefs, methods, approaches, innovations, growth, and its successes. There have been continuous attempts by the child serving system of care to control and rein-in Jasper Mountain. The organization has been told it was not needed, it was overstating the problem of child abuse, it must change the target population, it must change its beliefs and innovative methods, and generally speaking it must not stand out and must be like other organizations and not make waves. All available pressure points have been applied including: rule changes, investigations, political pressure, intimidation, and lawsuits to name a few. Although it may seem surprising that attempts to promote the best interests of children would develop adversaries from components of the system of care responsible to advocate for children, it may not be too surprising that innovation is not always met with support by bureaucracies.

With some reluctance, this brief description has been included for two reasons. First, Jasper Mountain has been forged in the fire of challenge not just in efforts to help the most difficult children, but also standing up to individuals or organizations with agendas that conflict with helping children. Although unpleasant and

213

unfortunate, this dynamic has been a part of the story of Jasper Mountain in the past and continues to this day. The second reason this adversarial dynamic has been included is that any individual or organization that seeks to help children must be prepared to speak out about precisely the areas of the system that are not promoting the best interests of children. Criticizing the status quo and persons and organizations in power positions is not likely to be met with gratitude. However, if the future is to change for disadvantaged children, then we must do a better job in our system of care to better prepare children for success. Jasper Mountain has always been willing to share the task, but someone must speak up when bureaucracies promote their self interests rather than the interests of children.

Including the controversy issue in the history of Jasper Mountain is not intended to communicate that the organization has always been right and everyone else wrong. We constantly self-reflect and adjust our approach. We have continually strived to be partners with the system and others working for children. In this effort we have attempted to go more than halfway to collaborate with others. There have been some exceptional individuals and organizations along the way who Jasper Mountain has worked with. It would have been great if everyone was willing to put personal agendas aside and work for the best interests of children, but this has not always been the case and because of this controversy has simply been an ever present reality we have had to address.

Program Components

There are many wonderful social service organizations. Some of the characteristics of highly effective service organizations are vision, passion and excellence in service delivery. These are the three legs to the stool that can bring a needed, effective and sustainable service to meet an important need. I want to provide some specific features that make Jasper Mountain the unique and effective organization that it is.

Within the last month I attended a professional training by an experienced professional concerning a well-known national approach to understand and work with problem behaviors in clients. The psychologist started the day by saying the following, "Neither I nor anyone else has the magical power to effect change inside of individuals. Since this is not possible, all we can do is to work with the external behaviors of individuals we all work with." I was impressed by the bluntness and honesty of this statement because he came right out and said what other approaches believe but communicate less clearly. This statement perhaps reflects the most fundamental difference between Jasper Mountain and many other approaches to human behavior. The difference is that not only do we believe the essence of real change is inside the individual, but for many years we have demonstrated this with thousands of individuals.

The thinking that internal change is so complex as to make it an impossibility is a holdover from the past. This way of thinking is the basis of Skinnerian behaviorism that puts the focus solely on external behaviors because that is all that we can see. However, this way of thinking has been brought into serious question by the last two decades of brain research. Skinner, Watson and the other behaviorists had only the most rudimentary knowledge of how the brain functioned and, for the most part, had to rely on external observable indicators of problems and solutions. But this is not the case today. We know a great deal about the antecedents of not only dysfunction but habilitation (which means to put health into practice). Externalized behavior is of interest and a

215

part of the process of treatment, but in the model used at Jasper Mountain the key is to change the individual from the inside out.

Practice Principles

In addition to the focus on changes within the brain, there are principles that guide the philosophy and inform the treatment programs of Jasper Mountain:

1) The family is the single most important influence in the shaping of a healthy or dysfunctional person.

2) Young, traumatized children heal optimally in a supportive treatment family context rather than in an institution.

3) For abused children, early family deficiencies can be rehabilitated under the right conditions; the younger the child, the better.

4) At an early age, human beings develop a fundamental disposition to the world – positive and trusting toward responsive caregivers, or anxious and fearful toward unresponsive caregivers.

5) A healthy environment breeds healthy interactions from healthy individuals.

6) Functioning fully is not a natural state for human beings; it must be taught through modeling and mastered through repeated practice.

7) The most fundamental requirement of the whole person is self-understanding.

Within these practice principles can be found how Jasper Mountain goes about effecting positive change in young children (our primary target population)—in a supportive treatment family environment, focusing on internal perceptual change, and modeling health of mind, body and spirit.

For many years there have been differing opinions as to whether children should receive mental health treatment in families or in residential settings. At Jasper Mountain we view this as a false dichotomy often used to support a preferred intervention. We believe that if a child can effectively receive the needed mental health treatment in his or her own family or therapeutic family, this would be the obvious choice. Because Jasper Mountain has a focus on the most challenging population, most of the children referred to us are not safe in families and need much more intensive intervention than can be provided in therapeutic family settings. However, at the point it is safe and feasible to impact change in the family setting, this will likely be the preferred setting. With the continuum of care at Jasper Mountain we can provide outpatient treatment with children living in their family home, in intensive wraparound care in the family, in a therapeutic foster family or, for the most intensive treatment, in a treatment family residential setting. In our view, no one setting is better than another, the optimal setting is a function of the needs of the child.

The Building Blocks of Treating Emotional and Behavioral Disturbance

Borrowing from Abraham Maslow and Eric Erikson, we have observed children healing in a predictable direction although not always in a linear fashion. The following are the building blocks or sign posts along the way of healing the mind, body and spirit of a child with an emotional or behavioral disturbance. A detailed discussion of these key components in the healing process can be found in *Raising Children Who Refuse To Be Raised* (Ziegler, 2000).

Safety—no healing can occur without safety and this can be the most difficult step. Without safety the child puts most of his or her energy into being anxious and fearful. The child must not only be in a safe supportive environment but experience this safety.

Security—the next step is stability that is provided by a predictable environment where negative surprises are avoided and the child can count on knowing what is going on and why in order to lower fear and anxiety and raise the level of enjoyment and learning.

Kirk's Depleted Ego

Kirk displayed significant behavioral dysregulation when faced with anything he perceived as challenging. He entered our program from his adoptive home where he regularly faced comparison to an overachieving sibling, developing a strong perception of himself as the disappointment of the family. Early in our work with him, Kirk played out the "bad kid" role and often attempted to harm himself, harm others, and recreate negative scenarios to convince himself he was correct in his belief that he deserved punishment. Cognitive behavioral therapy was used to support Kirk's cognitive restructuring of his self-view or inner working model, increasing his confidence in making positive decisions and enhancing his acceptance of positive feedback, something that once was so foreign to his view of himself. Though he struggled to gain control over sexual and aggressive impulses, he grew increasingly better at communicating that he could make positive choices and feel good about himself. It was a slow process but a key step for Kirk was a differentiation between who he was as a person on the inside and his external behaviors.

Jeff Huston, M.S., L.P.C.

Acceptance—the child must experience the difference between their behavior and who they are. Children with serious mental health issues often act in negative ways. The child must begin to see the difference between negative behavior and being a positive person.

Belonging—all human beings have a need to belong. A child will not reach out and be vulnerable unless the risk of being rejected is lessened by the experience of feeling connected and a part of something more than the self, such as a family.

Trust—this can be the most challenging step for children who have been mistreated or damaged by others. To trust is to be vulnerable and this can only begin when the brain detects that the advantages of connection outweigh the risks of disappointment.

Relationship—true relationship is the interplay of individuals where no one is used or abused. This step requires reciprocity, respect and an understanding of personal needs and the needs of others. The most important component of happiness is social support that can only be achieved from relationship.

Self-Awareness—we learn about ourselves through the mirror of others. Without connection with others internal reflection and subsequent growth and development are impossible. This step is the key to maximizing the unique qualities and gifts of the individual.

Personal Worth—the highest step in the process of growth is to internally recognize the intrinsic value of the self and be able to be resilient in the face of the challenges of daily living. This step includes the ability to have internal strength in the face of external personal attack.

The Five Fundamental Social Skill Sets — The Gemstones

Jasper Mountain teaches and supports children in developing the ability to become socially successful in life. The process of social success, which is a requirement of a truly successful life, is to develop the following five skill sets:

Thinking Smart — the ability to make smart decisions that are grounded in learning from past experience and optimizing the executive functions of the brain.

Self-Love/Self-Care — the ability to value yourself, take care of yourself and act in ways to promote your best interests.

Spiritual Health — to understand and put into practice the connection with others and being a part of something greater than the self.

Cooperation — the ability to get along with others through communication, compromise, and consideration.

Empathy — the recognition that others have needs, desires, and feelings and the ability to demonstrate an understanding of the experience of others.

Staff are trained to 'catch' the child demonstrating these positive skills and when this happens they receive a gold star that goes on a wall-mounted board. When a child has consistently shown an understanding and practice of these skill sets they are awarded a genuine gemstone by the Board of Directors in a ceremony. The gems come from Brazil and go into a display box that goes with the child when they graduate from the program to help them remember the importance of demonstrating these skills throughout life.

Trauma Treatment

The level of successful treatment at Jasper Mountain has surprised even us. The number of success indicators and the ways these are measured are different with each program. The details of the program's success will not be reported here due to length, but with the most challenging children, the program has repeatedly shown remarkable success. More can be found at the program's website www.jaspermountain.org. It has only been recently that we believe we can answer the question why the treatment is so successful. The answer is the combination of many factors but primarily the interplay of Neurological Reparative Therapy with trauma treatment. These two components work hand-in-hand to produce internal changes, alter the perceptual system used by the child's brain, and open up a world of learning and fun, which are the two primary tasks of a child.

Essentially all the children treated by Jasper Mountain have been traumatized and often the trauma has been chronic and, therefore, engrained into the brain of the child. With intensive trauma treatment, the child is supported though a process of internal healing that involves the ten fundamental steps of trauma work that are explained in the books *Traumatic Experience and the Brain* (Ziegler, 2002) and *Achieving Success With Impossible Children* (Ziegler, 2005). Trauma is one of the negative experiences of life that does not heal with time. The reason for this is that trauma alters the way the brain understands the world, it changes how the brain perceives and interprets events that occur, and trauma produces a biological stress response cycle that significantly impacts the emotions and behaviors of the individual (discussed in Chapter 5). With these negative impacts, the default mode of the brain becomes a negative and reactive process of self-protection through either avoidance or aggression. These patterns become habituated unless there is intervention to produce change in these internal processes.

We believe the surprising level of success after treatment at Jasper Mountain is due to changing the way the child's brain functions and eliminating the negative aspects of past trauma so the child can take advantage of the positive, supportive aspects of the individuals they can rely on for support and help in the future. This combination, in a real sense, gives children a fresh start and they have a great deal of fun and learning to catch up on since they no longer have to be responsible for their own personal safety.

Attachment Treatment

Another thread in the weave of successful treatment is improving the child's ability to connect and attach to care providers. Since the key to a successful life is the ability to positively navigate in a social world, the ability to connect and bond to others is essential. This process can be called the ability to form attachments. Several factors can negatively influence the instinctual process of attaching to a primary care provider. One negative influence to the attachment process early in life is trauma, particularly neglect. While trauma treatment can have a positive impact on improving the ability of a child to bond with a care provider, paying particular attention to the attachment process itself can be even more helpful.

A detailed treatment of rehabilitating the attachment process can be found in *Raising Children Who Refuse To Be Raised* (Ziegler, 2000) and *Achieving Success With Impossible Children* (Ziegler, 2005). Briefly stated, the process of repairing attachment can be broken down into four essential steps: 1. The child must experience the environment as safe, 2. Basic needs must be unconditionally met, 3. Constant invitations to connect must come from the adult to the child, and 4. Reciprocity must be taught where the child's wants (not needs) are conditional upon a two-way give and take process, a requirement of a positive relationship.

The importance of the role of repairing attachment in the larger picture of helping a damaged child heal cannot be overstated. To impact the ability of a client to bond with others forming a support system may be the single most significant change a treatment provider can facilitate to impact the long-term health of the individual. Attention to the attachment process should be a component of all mental health treatment in children, teens and adults.

Resiliency Training

Resiliency is the ability to bounce back after a negative experience. The ability to be resilient will determine an individual's success in weathering the challenges of living and prevailing. After trauma, the ability to be resilient can be damaged by the negative impacts on the brain of the traumatic experience. When resiliency is damaged it must be specifically learned again. A more detailed discussion of resiliency can be found in *Beyond Healing* (Ziegler, 2008). Resiliency is about acting, not reacting. Following trauma, the individual becomes much more reactive and this dynamic shuts down the person's ability to have a positive response to adversity. Learning to bounce back is an important part of the healing process and moving forward in life in a positive fashion.

Resiliency training involves helping the individual see the difference between acting and reacting. Self-awareness of biological states that cause anxiety and stress is a part of the process. Strategies to turn off stress such as relaxation, meditation, focus awareness, imagery, and others can teach the brain to become more confident in the face of pressure and stress. This process can be called self-mastery when the individual is able to positively influence their own internal experience producing the confidence to bounce back from adversity. The human condition includes continual difficulties where our plans do not work out as we wished. The ability to recover from adversity is a critically important aspect of a functional and positive life. The more practice at bouncing back from difficulties the individual has, the more resilient they become.

Childlike Play is an Important Aspect of Healing

In addition to the above components of the therapy process at Jasper Mountain, play is given special attention. A detailed section on this topic is included here because of how often play is overlooked. The primary task of every child comes down to two essential activities: playing and learning. These two activities are not mutually exclusive and both are enhanced by the other. New developments in brain research appear to indicate that children never lose their ability to learn, even under the worst of circumstances the child is learning either positive or negative lessons from their experiences and their environment. However, the ability to play is entirely a different matter.

The most admirable and attractive trait of a child is their "childlike" approach to the world. Although children go through intense socialization to mature and 'act your age' (often meaning to act older than you are), childhood can be a truly magical time of life where possibilities are endless and enjoyment can be found everywhere the child looks. For example, the young child on Christmas morning who opens a large present and is more interested in playing in the box than what the box contained. Adults admire the ability of children to take in the world with openness and enthusiasm. The spontaneity of childhood is something many adults long for after this approach to life is acculturated out of them as they grow older.

However, childhood can be a tragic time of life for the many children who experience significant trauma in their early years. While the ability to learn from experiences, despite how negative these may be, continues throughout childhood, the ability to experience childlike play is often a casualty of the trauma. The loss of childlike play is often a serious outgrowth of trauma. The importance of returning a sense of childlike playfulness is crucial.

Play may be the most important aspect of living that has no utilitarian purpose. Play is both an activity and a goal. Play is the purest form of re-creation or reinstating a sense of wholeness and well-being. Healthy children are either playing or looking for the next opportunity to do so. A child approaches play as a natural and necessary part of living. It is simply what they want to do and they seldom appear to get tired of it, although for everything else in life they seem to have a short attention span and can become quickly bored. For most children many activities of living take away energy—school work, cleaning their room, doing chores around the house. However play, regardless of how energetic, gives energy back to the child. Adults refer to such activity as recreation, meaning an activity that helps us re-create ourselves and gives us more enthusiasm for living.

True childlike play is not about competition where there is a winner and loser. In fact, children must learn the concept of playing with someone else and coming out ahead or behind, like in nearly all adult games. For children play is engagement in life and in connecting with others. To be involved in play is fun, but it is even better to play with playmates. Children who show no interest in social play raise concerns.

We are beginning to learn just how good of a job the human brain can do to promote physical and emotional healing. In fact, it appears that humans are preset to not only survive but to thrive throughout life (Diener & Diener, 1995). Just as people often lose the ability to enjoy living, they also gradually lose innate abilities to self-heal. For this reason childlike play should be encouraged for all children and specifically for children who have faced traumatic experiences.

Childlike play is creative, it is imaginative and it is nearly always active. This type of play is engrossing and all consuming. The child gets lost in play and loses the sense of time and all too often play must be discontinued for the boring and mundane aspects of living such as eating, bathing and sleeping. During childlike play the individual is focused on the process or playful act and not on the self or actor. In this way play is the antithesis to stressful activity.

Play encourages children to use their imagination, an important way that the child's brain develops. There are many other aspects of childhood play that teach children about issues such as roles, relationships, social interaction, the needs of others, and resolving conflict (or not). Even to address the question of why play is important for children is to miss the point somewhat. Play is a natural state of being for a child; it is what a child does. It is how a child learns to communicate and interact with others. The question of why is similar to asking why fish swim or birds fly. There may be utility in these activities but at the deepest level it is what they do. Play is what children do, that is unless they have been damaged by some form of traumatic experience.

The stress of traumatic experiences does immediate damage to a child's ability to engage in childlike play. Although some neuroscientists identify the loss of self-regulation as the most pervasive impact of trauma (van der Kolk, et. al., 1996), the loss of childlike play comes before this and is even more pervasive. The reasons for this are numerous, but begin with the definition of traumatic experience itself. Trauma is any experience that overrides the individual's ability to cope with the situation (Ziegler, 2000). When trauma occurs the human brain is faced with the primary issue it is designed to immediately address — a threat to survival. As soon as the brain identifies a survival threat, all brain functions are immediately targeted toward a response to the threat. This process takes place through the stress response cycle of perceiving and then responding with the fight or flight mechanism. When the brain recognizes a survival threat, the hippocampus signals corticotropin releasing factor that prompts the pituitary and adrenal glands of the body to release adrenaline, epinephrine and cortisol enabling the fight or flight response (Ziegler, 2008). Trauma can impair the hippocampus which helps put events into long-term memory storage by excessive cortisol release killing neurons (Brunson et. al., 2002).

The experience of traumatic stress can be considered the polar opposite of childlike play. Where play is imaginative, expressive and expanding by nature, stress is restricting, protective and confining for the individual. Play produces dopamine, a neurotransmitter associated with a sense of well-being, while traumatic stress produces hormones that put the brain and autonomic nervous system on red alert producing fear and even terror.

Even more concerning than immediate impacts of trauma are the long-range impacts of traumatic stress on childlike play. Unlike most adults who generally can sense when a threat has passed, children often do not accurately perceive the termination of a survival threat. The child's brain is so fundamentally designed to react to traumatic stress that it changes both perceptual experience and literally changes its structure (Ziegler, 2002). Lasting changes in the brain are designed to respond to any future threats. Unfortunately, children misperceive future threats and become stuck in a continual cycle of perceiving and reacting to traumatic stress (van der Kolk, et. al., 1996).

Trauma strikes at the very foundation of being a child in a world where physical and emotional survival requires receiving the protection of caring and supportive adults. When a child experiences a threat to his or her survival, the child cannot afford to delegate vigilance to adults who may or may not provide the needed protection. These children believe they must assume responsibility for their own safety. The result is that the child must move from enjoyment to vigilance and from imaginative play to continually scanning the environment for any hints of concern which they all too often find, whether the threat is real or perceived.

Although it has been known for some time that traumatic experiences adversely affect childlike play, little attention has been given to the role play should have in the treatment and healing of trauma. This oversight must be rectified in the homes, treatment programs and schools where traumatized children struggle to get by each day.

The primary message is that childlike play does not come naturally to children following traumatic experiences, in fact, play violates the priority of the child's brain. Without intervention trauma does not improve with time, on the contrary, it often heightens in serious symptomology. A hypervigilant young child can become an isolated and depressed older child. The social requirements of successful living become more complex and difficult as the child matures and traumatized children are ill-equipped to negotiate this complexity successfully.

When children lose their ability to engage in childlike play they change an opportunity into a vulnerability. If the child's brain misses the opportunity to develop essential components of imaginative enjoyment and stress reduction, the brain instead becomes vulnerable to high levels of overwhelming traumatic stress that results in the loss of enjoyment and positive social contact as well as fearfulness that over time has been linked to autoimmune disorders and physical disease (Felitti, et. al., 1998).

Play must become as big a priority for traumatized children as learning social skills, receiving immunizations, and psychological treatment. In a real way, childlike play provides the child with aspects of all three of these elements. Play is one of the best ways for children to learn social skills because children learn best when having fun. Immunizations build the immune system of the body and positive brain development can support marshaling the body's defenses. Psychological treatment is designed to help the child regain a sense of self and the positive components of childlike play do the same. Therefore play is treatment in its purest form.

It is important not to assume that a traumatized child is actively involved in childlike play. Close inspection will often result in noticing that play activity may be taking place but it is anything but childlike in nature. Traumatized children do engage in play activities but bring into their play the stress they feel in all aspects of life. Play often becomes totally focused on winning and losing. Control become critical, they become obsessed with rules and attempt to alter the process so they do not come out the losers. These children often get into conflicts, with the play activity ending with unpleasant social conflict. Each time these types of play occur, the child is one more step removed from childlike play.

Recommendations Concerning Childlike Play

Since play is adversely affected after traumatic experience, the question becomes how to help the child develop or regain a childlike sense of play. The place to begin is to first recognize the child's need for the benefits that childlike play provides. Most adults assume that play comes naturally for children. Since play comes naturally to most non-traumatized children but being serious does not, parents primarily stress responsibility and accountability. When parents of traumatized children stress serious issues and not play, they can make the problem worse. Beyond this important awareness, there are other suggested steps including the following:

Teaching the child to play — these children nearly always lose the understanding of what pure play is and how to go about it, so play must be specifically taught. This can be more challenging for adults than it may sound. Adults are much better at teaching a child to be serious, responsible and more 'grown up.' To teach a child to play, adults need to consider what childlike play entails and assist the child to do what does not come naturally.

Integrating play in daily living — we must integrate childlike play into all aspects of the lives of children who have experienced significant trauma. At home, play needs to be a part of weekend activities as well as weekday activities. In school, play needs to be encouraged both at recess and in the classroom. Children learn more when they are enjoying the learning experience.

Modeling play—We must model childlike play because child learn best through modeling. Modeling requires the adult to regain the ability to engage in activities that are enjoyable and have no specific purpose other than to have fun. Such activities are as valuable for the adult as for the child.

Assessing the child's ability to play—we must observe whether playfulness is something a child is capable of and whether they gravitate to playful experiences. When we assess, we can also determine if the child is improving with our help and interventions.

Promoting childlike play—we must design environments for traumatized children that encourage not only responsibility, good decisions, moral reasoning and other 'adult-like' traits, but also silliness, laughter, expression of all types and childhood enjoyment.

Finally we must recognize that if we allow traumatized children to grow up without childlike play, we are allowing them to head into adulthood without the natural experience of finding the fun and enjoyable aspects of all parts of living. To do so would make us complicit in the trauma the child has already experienced.

Humor and the Healing Environment

The equivalent to childlike play for adults is humor. Humorless individuals are difficult to be around for any period of time and settings devoid of laughter and people enjoying themselves make unhealthy work environments. In the same way you would not want to jump into the water to save a drowning person if you cannot swim, helping children and adults lighten up and take themselves and their troubles less seriously can only be facilitated by people who model this attribute.

On a personal note, humor is a very important component of my personal mental health. In every presentation I give and every book I write I make sure that humor is an ever present aspect of the process of learning and dealing with the heavy issues of life. This book is different by design. A team decision, that I agreed with, was to present the content of the book without interspersing humor throughout its pages. While this made sense, the importance of humor in maintaining personal mental health had to be mentioned so I am doing it here.

Humor has many related factors such as being light-hearted, enjoying oneself, being playful, good-natured kidding, and laughter. All of these components of humor have been shown to reduce stress and assist people to cope with the pressures of living and dying (Cousins, 1979; Miller, 2005; Berk, 2009).

Children and adults learn better when they are enjoying the process. Humor and laughter make an environment more enjoyable and less stressed. In all stressful occupations, certainly including social services, humor is essential to prevent vicarious traumatization and burnout. Therapy is one of the most stressful and challenging situations there is because sensitive issues must be looked at, painful issues must be explored, and uncomfortable changes must be made in the process. At the same time, the best therapy also includes humor and laughter.

Being playful and employing humor can be very useful to help children change their negative mood or avoid being stuck in a morose rut. Humor and sarcasm are very different, with the difference being the intent. Sarcasm uses humor to pointedly target someone with the intent to hurt them. There is no place for sarcasm in a healthy and healing environment. However, pointing out the irony of someone's actions or being factious to underscore a point when the intent is to be helpful can add humor to the process.

Despite humor not showing up in the descriptions of Neurological Reparative Therapy, the story of Jasper Mountain or the case examples, it is important to point out that Jasper Mountain is a place of laughter, humor and enjoyment. A healing environment must have these components to bring greater mental health to everyone, both consumers and staff. To put a bit of a spin on an old saying, 'if you lose your sense of humor, healing and living are just not very funny anymore.'

How Jasper Mountain Measures Success

The above are very brief descriptions of several aspects of the treatment approach used by Jasper Mountain. The overall success of the treatment model may be the way the various components are woven into a seamless process. A frequently asked question is what do you consider a successful outcome and how do you know if you are being successful?

Jasper Mountain staff do their best to go beyond the immediate crisis and the problem at hand and look deeper into the causes of negative symptoms. We look at symptoms like an iceberg where what you see above the surface is a small part of the problem and unless you can impact what is below the surface, you are likely to fail in intervening. This way of thinking does not fit well into the short-term focus of the managed-care model that currently pervades our national mental health system. Rationing care may be the most cost effective way to spread limited mental health service to as many individuals in need as possible, but it does not address the substantial needs of the most damaged populations in our mental health system. The current focus on restricting access to intensive and expensive mental health treatment is a shortsighted approach when it comes to traumatized children. There are so many negative outcomes later in life that can be prevented or affected by providing the in-depth treatment that children need as early in life as possible.

Therefore, success at Jasper Mountain is a function of symptom reduction for the immediate problem and repairing the brain and capacity-building for future success. An important question when providing mental health treatment to children is, 'what can be done now to improve the child's quality of life in ten years?' Without a long-term orientation, the child is relegated to a continual pattern of failing to cope with the stress of living.

To take a long-term view, the capacities of the individual are the primary indicators of success. Jasper Mountain has an outcome evaluation model that has two primary components — pre and post outcome assessment within the program and follow-up assessment at critical time frames following termination of services. Each of the programs have separate assessment measures. The goal is to have both standardized and criterion measures to assess outcomes. For each program there is a pre and post test on a variety of measures the first week and last week of treatment. If a child does not improve during treatment, it is unlikely they will do so following treatment. But the reverse cannot be reliably stated that success within the program will result in continued success following the conclusion of treatment.

While we are interested in improvement during treatment (by seeing symptom reduction and skill development), we are most interested in whether initial improvement continues or expands over time. To determine this we developed a list of twenty-one characteristics of a healthy individual. For example, measuring whether children drop out of school does not tell you if they are learning and growing. To do so we measure if the child is invested in learning, is setting goals, and is doing academic work at an appropriate level for their age and background. Similar measures involve investment in family life, making and keeping positive relationships, and demonstrating a range of skills necessary to function optimally in family and community settings. The brief answer to what we call success at Jasper Mountain is to build the capacity of the child to set personal goals and develop the skills to achieve these goals. Symptom reduction, the goal of many programs, is important but inadequate when a longer term view is considered.

Jasper Mountain is Only One Example

To conclude this discussion of Jasper Mountain, I want to explain why I have included this chapter in this book. Neurological Reparative Therapy is an orientation to the healing process. By itself it is a framework of the treatment structure without the essential details of application. Jasper Mountain is one example of applying this orientation in a continuum of service programs. Every social service organization is and should be unique and designed to meet its mission and address the needs of its target population. I wanted to give the reader an overview of a setting where NRT has been effectively integrated. More information is available on the approaches and services of Jasper Mountain on its website www.jaspermountain.org. Neurological Reparative Therapy is a roadmap to healing, but the vehicle to reach the destination is both the human contact of the helping individual and the framework of an effective service. Jasper Mountain is only one of a myriad of ways NRT can be applied in a practical and effective way.

Epilogue

Why Neurological Reparative Therapy is Not the Full Answer

Neurological Reparative Therapy brings a new perspective based upon exploding new brain science to the work of helping people understand their inner and outer world. However, it does not purport to be the full answer to the question of how best to help individuals who struggle in life. It is a new model with many advantages over previous models of therapy, but like a new model automobile, over time new information and advancements will move us beyond our current understanding. The wonders of the human brain are presently in the early stages, not late stages, of discovery. The hubris of the early twentieth century writer must be avoided when he said surely we stand on the verge of having invented all that human beings are capable of. In the not too distant future, we will look back upon our current knowledge of the brain and more fully appreciate how much more there is to know about the most important frontier of science — the human brain, with its gateway to who we are and how we comprehend the world around us.

We must view the study of psychology as a science in its infancy. My own forty-year career has seen enormous changes in our perspectives on motivation, emotions, memory, behavior, the subjective mind and the human potential. And yet, the field of psychology is just over 100 years old and I have been alive half of this time and a practitioner for more than a third of the time psychology has been a discipline. My point is that we are just beginning to develop both the information and the wisdom to integrate new knowledge into efforts to understand and help people live better lives. As in any science, every new discovery opens new doors to further discovery and so shall it be with understanding the human brain. While we are advanced enough in brain science to realize some of what we do not yet know, such as how the mind inhabits the brain and how the various regions of the brain work together for simple and complex tasks, we as yet do not know the right questions much less the answers to understand the most complex organic structure in the universe — the human brain.

As was explained in the first chapter, Neurological Reparative Therapy is an overarching conceptual model that can be a framework for treatment and for the development of interventions. It is a roadmap, but it is not the vehicle which would be the skill, expertise and therapeutic orientation of the therapist. Regardless of any amount of research, a great tool in the hands of a mediocre craftsman is going to produce mediocre results. While important, the emphasis on evidence-based practices has overshadowed a much more important component of positive outcomes and that is the competence of the practitioner (Norcross, 2002). The components of competence are many: insight into the self, years of education and training in aspects of the helping profession, integration of the strengths of the therapist with a philosophical and therapeutic approach, years of supervision, years of direct clinical experience. There are no shortcuts to clinical competence, and even after completing all these steps, excellence is by no means insured.

Clinical competence is a given when it comes to using NRT as a model. The model will not teach or make someone competent if they are not there to start with. With clinical competence, NRT can be learned and put into practice with no more background and training than is provided in this book. It takes years to become a competent and effective therapist, but implementing NRT as a therapeutic model can be implemented with a good understanding of the goals in Chapter 4 and the steps of the model in Chapter 5. If NRT informed interventions are desired, the process has been explained in some depth in Chapter 6 and used in case examples in Chapters 7, 8 and 9.

There are many very good therapists who have worked in the field for some time who have a growing discomfort that new information is coming out on the brain that was not a part of their education or their professional training. Thousands of these professionals are looking for trainings in the United States and other countries as well. For these skilled and competent therapists eager to incorporate new understandings of the brain, Neurological Reparative Therapy may be at least part of the answer. As a treatment model it cannot be in its final form, a vibrant model must adjust as information becomes available. At the same time, just because more will be learned about the brain over the next decade, it does not make sense to wait until sometime in the future to be able to define what we do in psychological treatment in relation to the brain. All treatment must focus on the brain and every therapeutic approach must account for how the approach and accompanying techniques impact the brain.

It is my hope that the reader will find this new model of use to enhance what you already do well, and improve what you are doing that may at present be producing less than optimal results. In every country, region, city and rural community throughout the world there are individuals who struggle to cope with the stress and demands of daily life. Many of these individuals need support and direction from a helping professional. I want to express my personal appreciation for the selfless investment you put into the struggling people you help. I often conclude my training with the following comments. We live in an American society that seems to have become confused as to who and what a hero is. Ask children and they will tell you that they want to be a hero when they grow up. But the heroes held up to children are far too often athletes, rock stars, and Hollywood celebrities. As skilled at their craft as these individuals may be, they are not heroes. To be a hero is not notoriety, wealth or even unique skill. To be heroic is about courage and bravery in a noble endeavor. For the media this may be an overpaid athlete in a Super Bowl, but for me the most noble of endeavors is to lighten the load of another person by supporting and assisting them in finding a better life. To the degree that you do this, I include you in my category of heroes. The helping professions do not have Oscars, Grammy's, Championship Rings, or All-American Teams. We do what we do quietly and one person at a time. None of us get into the business of helping people to get special attention and awards. You may work your entire career with no specific acknowledgement of all that you do except for the occasional client who recognizes some of the worth of what you have provided. Many of the other people you help may not even appreciate you at the time. So please accept my respect and my thanks for all you do to help others.

Appendices

Neurological Reparative Therapy Intervention Protocol

The following process can be utilized to develop interventions under the NRT model. It is designed to proceed step-by-step through the process of identifying the right problem by considering the meaning of the target symptom to the child, learning what the child is actually saying to adults, considering the background causes, developing specific interventions, and ending with monitoring and adjusting interventions over time.

Step 1 — Define the specific target symptom to address:

- Decide where to start, you may not want to take on the biggest issue first or you may choose to do just that.

- Choose a target symptom that can be observed and measured.

- Be specific and detailed, avoid "He is always angry," instead "He responds with intense anger when he is told he is wrong and needs to redo his school work."

Target Symptom Statement:

_____

_____

_____

_____

_____

_____

Step 2 — Identify the meaning of the target symptom to the child.

A. Translate the meaning of the behavior:

- List the possible translations of the child's behavior, come up with at least 7 but not more than 12.
- Make sure at least two are "thinking outside the box" translations.

_____	_____
_____	_____
_____	_____
_____	_____
[_____]	[_____]

Now have the person who best knows the child in the context of the target symptom place a "-" before the translations that do not fit, a "+" before the translations that do fit, and a "++" if the translation fits to a significant degree. Combine the endorsed translations, particularly the ++ and put the translations together to come up with the 'most likely' translation of the meaning of the behavior to the child. It may be wrong but it will be the best educated guess.

B. Learning the meaning of the child's words related to the target symptom:

Frequent statements   Opposite meaning

_____	_____
_____	_____

_____   _____
_____   _____
_____   _____
_____   _____
_____   _____
_____   _____
_____   _____

Many children with emotional and behavioral problems speak in opposites. Rephrase the child's statements with the opposite meaning on the right side of the form. Circle which you believe to be more accurate for the child.

To complete Step 2 combine the most likely meaning of the target symptom with the most accurate statements. The following is the working translation of the target symptom:

_____
_____
_____
_____
_____
_____

Step 3 — Consider causes of the target symptom.

Review the child's background with particular attention to any trauma history. Consider the perceptions of the child represented in the meaning of the behavior in Step 2. What links exist between the child's history and the child's perceptions? If there are links between the two, this is likely the underlying cause of the target symptom. Knowing the cause provides the best likelihood of an effective intervention.

Trauma history

_____

_____

_____

Family and developmental history

_____

_____

_____

_____

Step 4 — Develop a list of potential interventions.

- Consider multiple interventions
- Include interventions supported by the environment of the child
- Start with a manageable number of interventions (2-5)
- Insure each intervention specifically addresses the meaning and causes of the target symptom.

_____

_____

_____

_____

_____

_____

_____

_____

_____

_____

_____

_____

_____

Step 5 — Evaluate what is and is not working with the interventions.

- Determine a timeline to assess the effectiveness of each intervention
- Avoid putting too much faith in any one intervention
- Do not expect to find gold in the first shovel of gravel
- Expect to revise all interventions, even the ones that are effective; what works today may not work tomorrow.
- Even if the target symptom improves, it is likely that other target symptoms will need to be addressed and with a new target symptom begin again at Step 1.
- Model to everyone in the child's world that improvement is a long process with many course corrections along the way.

Preventing Trauma — Teaching Children to Cope

The primary difference between trauma and resiliency is the ability to cope with a difficult situation. Like many other skills that are needed throughout life, the ability to cope does not come naturally to children or adults, it must be taught and learned. Coping with a potentially traumatic situation actually goes against the body and brain's process of handling stressful events. The brain naturally sounds the alarm that something bad is happening and the body's autonomic and sympathetic nervous systems naturally respond by instituting the stress response often leading to fight/flight behaviors. If the goal is to go against what comes naturally in the brain and the body, then the individual counters thousands of years of genetic and developmental selection. Just how can this be accomplished? The following is a short form of the Neurological Reparative Therapy model in a somewhat different format. There are twelve critical components that make the difference between someone capable of managing most of the stresses in life and someone who is overcome or even traumatized by the experience. These twelve components can be found in COPERS who use COPING skills routinely in difficult situations.

Our goal is to teach children to be COPERS when it comes to stressful life situations and events. COPERS have the following attributes and skills:

Connections and attachment with others. Our very first instinct after we are born is to attach to our mothers. As we mature our social connections expand to others in the family, neighbors, teachers, peers and the social circle continues to expand outward. Happiness in life and the ability to manage the inevitable problems of living are directly related to the social support we have at every developmental period of life from birth to death.

O ptimism and a positive outlook. We live in the world that we perceive and experience. The greatest impact on our experience is whether we chronically have a positive or negative outlook. Our perceptions lead to our emotions and emotions lead to behaviors and all three determine how we experience everything around us. When we expect good things, there is a much better chance that good things will happen.

P lay and recreation. There is a reason we refer to enjoyable activities as recreation or re-creating ourselves. Play is one of the two primary components of the job description of a child (the other is to learn). Play is about interfacing with the natural environment. It is about imagination and possibilities. Play has no purpose, it is a goal unto itself. For children and adults, we rebuild our bodies, our energy level, and our enthusiasm through play.

E xercise and aerobic activity. Exercise is focused play that activates the mind, body and spirit all at once. The best exercise engages all of the person as in aerobic activity that works the muscles, bones, joints, skin, and the body's systems such as respiration and circulation. Aerobic exercise is not just good for staying fit with a well-tuned body, we now know it is a key to brain health. Like a race horse, our bodies are naturally designed to be worked.

R esiliency and persistence. Resiliency is the ability to bounce back following adversity. Bad things happen in everyone's life, but some individuals can come back strong after a negative experience and others are weakened. The ability to persist in the face of obstacles and difficulties defines the individual that not only can cope with adversity but is strengthened by challenges throughout life.

S tress reduction. The human body is preset to respond in significant ways to stress, as well it should. However, chronic stress means chronic activation of the stress response cycle and the result is damage to all aspects of a person's mind, body and spirit. The antidote to stress is relaxation and the ability to turn off the stress response of the body's nervous system and the brain's limbic reactivity. A fulfilling life demands the ability to manage and reduce stress.

COPERS are able to face stressful situations by swimming with the tide and staying afloat. They do not fight the tide but work with it to keep their head above water. They do this by COPING with events that overwhelm many others who often experience a significant stress as a traumatic experience with potentially serious and lasting negative impacts. COPING involves these important characteristics and abilities:

C oncentration and focused attention. A healthy brain is important to overall physical health. The brain requires exercise and conditioning to be in optimal shape. Either the brain has internal control or it is at the mercy of external stimuli. Concentration and focused attention is the key to optimizing the ability of the brain to be self-directed and internally managed. Without this critical skill we are unable to put our brain and our mind to the tasks we find important.

O ptimum mental health. We are healthy of mind when we use our innate ability to heal and thrive. The regions of the brain must work together to maintain and manage the body, understand and make effective use of emotions and not be overcome by them, and empower the frontal lobes to use executive functions to perceive and achieve. Optimal brain health requires mental flexibility and maximizing the brain's most specialized and complex abilities.

P erseverance and problem-solving. When adversity strikes the first step in a positive response is to weather the storm and address the situation as positively as possible. This requires the ability to accurately perceive the situation and connect problems with potential solutions requiring higher order reasoning. Once a plan is developed the most important trait of a healthy individual is perseverance and sticking to the task at hand.

I nvolvement in a social network. Like neurons in the brain, people must be connected to others to survive and thrive. Our social connections are critical to everything we do in life from working, playing, praying, and living to the fullest. Having a social network, such as a family, is not enough, we also need to invest and involve ourselves in the social networks we have. The level of engagement and involvement is directly connected to how much we get back.

N euro-integration. The human brain is capable of amazing synergy or unimaginable chaos. The billions of neurons carrying continual sensory data throughout the brain require internal organization to avoid total confusion. Neuro-integration is the ability of the regions of the brain to work in harmony producing more than the sum of the parts. Having mental abilities is only valuable to the degree that these abilities can be coordinated and harnessed.

G oal setting. As the saying goes, if you don't know where you are going then any road will get you there. The first step in goal setting is to develop a plan to reach a desired outcome. Goal setting is one of the most important executive functions coming from the orbitofrontal cortex of the human brain. Goals enable us to be self-directed and internally driven, which is the opposite of being a reactive victim to the hardships everyone experiences.

The above twelve traits and skills are the foundation upon which to build a life that faces hardship and challenges and becomes stronger because of them. These are the critical components of the healing, resiliency and well-being in the Neurological Reparative Therapy model. These abilities make the difference from being a victim to not just being a survivor, but thriving in life. Humans are born with the potential to achieve their dreams and, perhaps, even change the world, but this potential must be actualized through teaching, guidance and modeling. If we want our children to succeed in life then they deserve to have the best available tools. These twelve components of COPERS who use COPING in everyday life have the potential to make all the difference between struggling to get by and living life to its fullest.

The Direct Care Treatment Plan, Two Treatment Plans for Every Child

More is not always better, but in the treatment of children with emotional and behavioral disturbances two treatment plans can be better than one. The causes of emotional and behavioral problems in children are many and thus the solutions to these problems can be complex and must be individualized. And yet children are children and they all have the same basic needs for safety, security, acceptance, belonging, food, shelter, love and touch to name a few of the most important basic needs. Psychological treatment must be targeted and individualized, but providing the same basic needs and building blocks for a successful future to every child leads to the consideration that two treatment plans may be better than one.

The targeted clinical treatment plan is very familiar in every intensive and outpatient treatment setting. Such a plan involves careful assessment, identification of the target problems (diagnosis), and designing sophisticated interventions that address the causes and solutions to the unique problems of the individual child. These Clinical Treatment Plans (CTP) are the foundation of our mental health system. They usually involve a collaboration of parents with professionals all working to implement a plan to help alleviate problematic symptoms and return a child to a state of healthy functioning. When treatment plans are mentioned, it is the CTP that people are referencing.

At the same time a targeted and individualized plan is essential to help a struggling child, all children have the same basic needs that will form the foundation for a lifetime of either success or failure depending upon how these basic needs are met. Every struggling child could also use a second treatment focus that addresses the universal basic needs of every child. The job of a young child is to live in the present, but the job of a parent is to keep an eye on the future. The healthy child engages with the world around him or her through learning and playing in the present with little attention or interest in the future. However, the parent must not only provide for the present needs of the child but must prepare the child for the future with tools that will promote success throughout life.

The fundamental role of all adults who help children is to be a parent who both meets the immediate needs of the child and prepares the child for the future. Direct care staff in treatment programs often ask how they can optimize their ability to be helpful in the treatment process of children in settings such as schools, community-based programs, and residential settings. One way to do this is through implementing a second treatment plan for every child, what will be called the Direct Care Treatment Plan (DCTP). This plan addresses the universal needs of every child regardless of the emotional or behavioral problems that have brought the child and family to the treatment setting. The Clinical Treatment Plan may require specific psychiatric and psychological components primarily addressed by professionals in specific settings. However the Direct Care Treatment Plan can be the primary focus of both direct care staff as well as parents of the child, moving in a collaborative direction.

The components of this second treatment plan must address what every child needs and answers the question of every direct care provider and parent, "How can I best help this child become better adjusted?" For the sake of clarity the universal steps of the DCTP are broken into the three D's of Disconfirming, Developing and Directing.

The Three D's

Disconfirmation *of past negative connections with others* (overcoming the past) – in many cases the emotional and behavioral problems of children in treatment settings have developed through negative patterns of interactions, primarily with adults. These negative interactions may either be trauma producing abuse and/or neglect or unsuccessful attempts by adults to manage the child's problems creating habitual negative patterns. Children quickly learn to adapt to situations through habitual behaviors that can often be negative such as: tantruming, lying, manipulation, aggression, stealing, avoiding, self-harm and many other symptom behaviors that usually form the presenting problems in treatment settings. These habitual patterns of adapting to people and situations will continue unless somehow disrupted. The first step of the DCTP is to disconfirm the belief in the child's mind that patterns of connection with others will continue and the end results will continue to be the same as they have been in the past.

Developing *a new inner working model* (reclaiming the present) – children function in the world based upon inner perceptions that can be called the child's inner working model. These perceptions have been formed from past experiences, often negative, and form the way the child understands the people and events the child encounters. The inner working model of children in treatment settings should be the main focus, rather than the emotions and behaviors that give rise from the inner model. Negative inner working models often view others as threatening rather than supporting, and the actions of others as harmful rather than having the intention to be helpful. Children in treatment settings misconstrue the motivations of adults and peers leading to adversarial interactions. Inner working models are also habitual in that they persist until something occurs to form a new inner working model or new way to perceive the self, others and events. After negative connections with others are disconfirmed, in other words the child learns old negative patterns will not be repeated, then new perceptions must form a more open and positive inner working model.

Directing *the child toward a successful future (preparing for the challenges ahead)* – because the role of parenting requires a focus on the future and not just on the present, continual attention must be given to teaching the child skills for present and future success. Too often adults focus on getting through a situation without sufficient focus on teaching the child how to do better the next time. This important step must be provided by adults because there are many skills the child will need that do not develop naturally. Without direction children do not learn essential skills such as reciprocity, empathy, self-control, responsibility, delayed gratification, moral values, consideration of others, and moving away from an egocentric focus. It is important to remember that the child naturally develops a primary focus on self and "What's in it for me." Learning to consider the needs and desires of others rather than self does not develop naturally. Without adults to direct this learning, progress in these areas will be slow, delayed, or never learned at all.

Implementing the Three D's

Unlike the CTP, the DCTP can be universally applied to all children regardless of the situation. Therefore, from the first contact to the last interaction with any child, the DCTP can be a blueprint on how to work with all children, whether the adult has significant information or no knowledge of the child's history.

There are many ways to implement the three D's including the following:

Disconfirmation of past negative connections with others

- Do your best to present energy toward the child that communicates safety, firmness, and remaining unruffled when tested by the child or situations that arise.
- Genuinely listen to the child and reflect an understanding of what the child is communicating by words, energy and non-verbal messages.
- Provide structure for the child, including setting limits.
- Communicate in multiple ways a sense of belonging in the environment.
- Decline all invitations to replicate past negative interactions with the child.

Developing a new inner working model

- First find the child's strengths and then point them out repeatedly.
- Accept the child even when you do not accept the behavior.
- Communicate a message of caring for the child.
- Engage with the child in play.
- Be consistent and repetitive in the above interactions.

Directing the child to a successful future

- Help the child build a sense of a positive self.
- When correcting mistakes let the child know you believe he/she can do better.
- Teach the child to self-regulate.

- Develop an attachment with the child built upon safety and personal interest.
- Reflect to the child how to prepare for the future.

Cook Book Recipes as Approaches to Treatment

Many new direct care staff ask a reasonable question, "What should I do with challenging children to get the best results?" Parents often ask the same question. While the question is reasonable, it is difficult to answer from a strictly clinical perspective. Clinical treatment requires a thorough assessment and knowledge of a child's development, genetics, family history, abilities and challenges. Added to this are the unique ways that a child's past creates difficulties in understanding behaviors. There are no cookbook recipes or 'one size fits all' clinical plans. However, the Direct Care Treatment Plan does not require weeks of assessment and years of education and training because the DCTP directly addresses the same needs that all children have—healing and learning from the past and engaging in the present while preparing for the future. There is still room for individualizing interventions for particular children. Under each of the headings and specific steps mentioned above, there are many ways to accomplish the objective and children respond differently so there is plenty of room for creativity and innovation.

There is no conflict between the CTP and the DCTP because one addresses universal needs and the other individualizes unique interventions for each child, and these two plans can and must be compatible and in-sync with each other. Optimally, direct care staff and parents will also assist with the CTP, but addressing the DCTP may be sufficient.

One of the many advantages of intensive treatment settings is not merely the significant amount of clinical treatment children receive but the hundreds of contacts with direct care workers that can often make all the difference between a successful outcome or further solidifying the negative perceptions and behaviors of children with emotional and behavioral disturbances. The DCTP is also one of the best methods to have the child's family and the treatment program on the same page. Family members may not be able to intervene with the child in some of the clinical interventions and services, but they can always be therapeutic agents with the child by following the Direct Care Treatment Plan.

If two treatment plans are better than one for children with emotional and behavioral disturbances, the question could be asked which plan will make the most difference. This question should be simply academic if both plans are being implemented well, however, many decades of research may help answer this question. The research on clinical interventions have repeatedly shown that some approaches work better than others. This is the basis for the term "evidence-based practice." However, there is strong support in research to common elements in effective practices. These common elements happen to correspond directly to the ingredients of the Direct Care Treatment Plan—when communicating with someone who really listens in a supportive relationship, new insights are provided, self-regulation is taught, perceptions are changed, and repetitive practice solidifies improvement. In asking which treatment plan may be most effective in helping a struggling child, research has for decades supported the fact that it is the person who offers a positive relationship to the client that helps more than the technique the person uses. From this perspective, the DCTP is the better match of the two treatment plans with research findings on effectiveness.

References and Suggested Reading

Asay, T.P. and Lambert, M.J. (1999). The Empirical Case for the Common Factors in Therapy: Quantitative Findings. In M.A Hubble, B. Duncan, S.D. Miller (Eds.). *The Heart & Soul of Change: What Works in Therapy.* The American Psychological Association. Washington, DC.

Bach–y-Rita, P. (1972). *Brain mechanisms in sensory substitution.* New York: Academic Press.

Bach-y-Rita, P., Collins, C.C., Saunders, F.A., White, B. & Scadden, L. (1969). Vision substitution by tactile image projection. *Nature, 221*(5184), 963-964.

Bauer, P.J. (2005). Developments in declarative memory: Decreasing susceptibility to storage failure over the second year of life. *Psychological Science, 16(1),* 41-47.

Beecher. H.K. (1955). The powerful placebo, *Journal of American Medical Association 159*(17).

Begley, S. & Yarett, I. (2011). Can you build a better brain? *Newsweek,* 1/10 (157), 40-45.

Benedetti, F., Mayberg, H.S., Wager, T.D., Stohler, C.S. & Zubieta, J. (2005). Neurobiological Mechanisms of the Placebo Effect. *The Journal of Neuroscience, 25*(45).

Bergin, A.E. & Garfield, S.L. (Eds.) (1994). *Handbook of Psychotherapy And Behavior Change, 4th Edition.* New York: Wiley.

Berk, L. (2009). Laughter remains good medicine. *American Psychological Society*. Washington, DC.

Bernstein, A. (2003). University of Michigan Study Finds Volunteering Reaps Health Rewards. Knight Ridder/Tribune Business News http://www.accessmylibrary.com/coms2/summary_0286-7968698_ITM.

Bowlby, J. (1982). *Attachment*. New York, Basic Books.

Brown, S. L., Nesse, R., Vinokur, A. D., & Smith, D. M. (2003). Providing Support may be More Beneficial than Receiving It: Results from a Prospective Study of Mortality. *Psychological Science, 14*, 320-327.

Brunson, K.L., Grigoriadi, D.E., Lorang, M.T. & Baram, T.Z. (2002). Corticotropin-releasing hormone (CRH) downregulates the function of its receptor (CRF1) and induces CRF1 expression in hippocampal and cortical regions of the immature rat brain. *Experimental Neurology*, 176(1), 75-86.

Cavada, C., & Schultz, W. (2000). The Mysterious Orbitofrontal Cortex. *Cerebral Cortex, 10*, 205.

Cousins, N. (1979). *Anatomy of an Illness: as Perceived by the Patient.* New York: W.W. Norton.

Curry, J.F., Wells, K.C., Brent, D.A., Clarke, G.N., Rohde, P., Albano, A.M., Reinecke, M.A., Benazon, N. & March, J.S. (2005). Treatment for Adolescents with Depression Study (TADS), Duke University Medical https://trialweb.dcri.duke.edu/tads/tad/manuals/TADS_CBT.pdf.

Davidson, R.J. (2004). Well-being and affective style: neural substrates and biobehavioral correlates. *Philosophical Transactions of the Royal Society of London.* B359, 1395-1411.

Davidson, R.J., Lewis, M., Alloy, L.B., Amaral, D.G., Bush, G. & Cohen, J. (2002). Neural and behavioral substrates of mood and mood regulation. *Biological Psychiatry, 52*(6), 478-502.

Denham, S. (1998). *Emotional Development in Young Children.* New York: Guilford.

Diener, E. & Biswas-Diener, R. (2008). *Happiness. Unlocking the Mysteries of Psychological Wealth.* Blackwell Publishing: Malden Massachusetts.

DeBellis, M.D., Baum, A., Birmaher, B., Keshaven, M.S., Eccard, C.H. & Boring, A.M. (1999). Developmental traumatology. Part 1: Biological stress systems. *Biological Psychiatry, 45,* 1259-1270.

Denham, S.A. (1997). "When I have a bad dream, my Mommy holds me": Preschooler's conceptions of emotions, parental socialization, and emotional competence. *International Journal of Behavioral Development, 20*: 301-319.

Diener, E., & Diener, C. (1995). Cross-cultural correlates of life satisfaction and self-satisfaction and self-esteem. *Journal of Personality and Social Psychology, 68,* 653-663.

Doidge, N. (2007). *The Brain That Changes Itself.* New York: Penguin Group.

Eisenberg, N., Fabes, R., Gutrie, I. & Reiser, M. (2000). Dispositional emotionality and regulation: Their role in predicting quality of social functioning. *Journal of Personality and Social Psychology, 78,* 136-157.

Fagiolini, M. & Hensch, T.K. (2000). Inhibitory threshold for critical-period activation in primary visual cortex. *Nature, 404(6774),* 183-186.

Felitti, V.J., Anda, R.F., Nordenberg, D., Williamson, D.F., Spitz, A.M., Edwards, V., & Koss, M.P. (1998). The relationship of adult health status to childhood abuse and household dysfunction. *American Journal of Preventive Medicine, 14,* 245-258.

Fries, A.B., Ziegler, T.E., Kurian, J.R., Jacoris, S. & Pollak, S.D. (2005). Early experience in humans is associated with changes in neuropeptides critical for regulating social behavior. *Proceedings of the National Academy of Sciences, USA, 102(47),* 17237-17240.

Gaensbauer, T.J., & Hiatt, S.W. (1984). Facial communication of emotion in early infancy. *Journal of Pediatric Psychology, 9,* 205-217.

Grafman, J. & Litvan, I. (1999). Evidence for four forms of neuroplasticity. In J. Grafman and Y. Christen (Eds.). *Neuronal plasticity: Building a bridge from the laboratory to the clinic.* Berlin: Springer-Verlag.

Greenberg, M.T., Speltz, M.L. & DeKlyen, M. (1993). The role of attachment in the early development of disruptive behavior problems. *Development and Psychopathology, 5,* 191-213.

Hariri A.R. & Holmes A. (2006). Genetics of emotional regulation: The role of the serotonin transporter in neural function. *Trends in Cognitive Science 10,* 182-191.

Heim, C., Nemeroff, C.B. (1999). The impact of early adverse experiences on brain systems involved in the pathophysiology of anxiety and affective disorders. *Biological Psychiatry 46*(11), 1509-1522.

Heim, C., Newport, D.J., Bonsall, R., Miller, A.H. & Nemeroff, C.B. (2001). Altered pituitary-adrenal axis responses to provocative challenge tests in adult survivors of childhood abuse. *American Journal of Psychiatry, 158(4)*, 575-581.

Henshaw, S.P. & Anderson, C.A. (1996). Conduct and oppositional defiant disorders. In E.J. Mash and R.A. Barkley (Eds.) *Child Psychopathology*, New York: Guilford Press.

Hindman, J. (2006) *There Is No Sex Fairy: To Protect Our Children From Becoming Sexual Abusers.* AlexAndria Associates.

Hinshaw, S.P., & Anderson, C.A. (1996). Conduct and oppositional defiant disorders. In E. Mash & R. Barkley (Eds.), *Child Psychopathology.* New York: Guildford, pp. 113-154.

Hughes, J.T. (1991). *Thomas Willis (1621-1675): His Life and Work,* London: Royal Society of Medicine.

Jacobs, B.L., van Praag, H. & Gage, F.H. (2000). Depression and the birth and death of brain cells. *American Scientist, 88(4),* 340-346.

Jacobs, B., Schall, M. & Scheibel, A.B. (1993). A quantitative dendritic analysis of Wernicke's area in humans. *Journal of Comparative Neurology, 327*(1): 97-111.

Johnson, K., Knitzer, J., & Kaufmann, R. (2002). *Making Dollars Follow Sense: Financing early childhood mental health services to promote healthy social and emotional development in young children.* New York: National Center for Children in Poverty.

Kagan, J. (2010). *The Temperamental Threat: How Genes, Culture, Time and Luck Make Us Who We Are.* New York: Dana Press.

Kandel, E.R. (2003). The molecular biology of memory storage: A dialog between genes and synapses. In H. Jornvall (Ed.) *Nobel Lectures, Physiology or Medicine, 1996-2000.* Singapore: World Scientific Publishing.

Kandel, E. R. (2007). *In Search of Memory: The Emergence of a New Science of Mind*, New York: W. W. Norton & Company.

Kaptchuk, T.J. (1998). Intentional Ignorance: a history of blind assessment and placebo controls in medicine. *Bulletin of the History of Medicine, 72*(3), 389-433.

Lambert, M.J. & Bergin, A.E. (1994). The effectiveness of psychotherapy. In A.E. Bergin and S.L. Garfield (Eds.), *Handbook of Psychotherapy and Behavior Change.* New York: John Wiley & Sons.

Lyubomirsky, S., King, L. & Diener, E. (2005). The benefits of frequent positive affect: Does happiness lead to success? *Psychological Bulletin, 131,* 803-855.

MacMillan, M. (2000). *An Odd Kind of Fame: Stories of Phineas Gage.* Cambridge MA: MIT Press.

MacMillan, M. (2008). Phineas Gage – Unraveling the myth. *The Psychologist (British Psychological Society), 21(9)*, 828–831.

McEwen, B.S. (2000). The neurobiology of stress: From serendipity to clinical relevance. *Brain Research, 886*, 172-189.

McEwen, B.S. (2008). Central effects of stress hormones in health and disease: Understanding the protective and damaging effects of stress and stress mediators. *European Journal of Pharmacology, 583*, 174-185.

McEwen, B.S. & Sapolsky, R.M. (1995). Stress and cognitive function. *Current Opinion in Neurobiology, 5(2)*, 205-216.

Melzer, M. & Poglitch, G. (1998). Functional changes in 100 children with autistic spectrum disorders. Presentation to the American Speech, Language and Hearing Association.

Miller, M. (2005). Laughter and Blood Flow, University of Maryland Medical Center, presented at the Scientific Session of the American College of Cardiology on March 7, 2005, in Orlando, Florida.

National Scientific Council on the Developing Child (2005). Excessive Stress Disrupts the Architecture of the Developing Brain: Working Paper #3. http://www.developingchild.net.

Nemeroff, C. B. (1996). The corticotropin-releasing factor (CRF) hypothesis of depression: New findings and new directions. *Molecular Psychiatry, 1*: 336-342.

Nietzsche, F. (1888). Twilight of the Idols, or, How to Philosophize with a Hammer. New York: Penguin Classics (1990).

Norcross, J. (Ed.) (2002). *Psychotherapy Relationships that Work, Therapist Contributions and Responsiveness to Patients*. New York: Oxford University Press.

Ornish, D. (1998). *Love & Survival - 8 Pathways to Intimacy and Health*. New York: Harper Collins.

Perry, B.D. (1994). Neurobiological sequelae of childhood trauma: PTSD in children. In M.M. Murburg (Ed.), *Catecholamine Function in Posttraumatic Stress Disorder: Emerging Concepts*. Washington, DC: American Psychiatric Press.

Pascual-Leone, A. Dang, N., Cohen, L.G., Brasil-Neto, J.P., Cammarota, A. & Hallett, M. (1995). Modulation of muscle responses evoked by transcranial magnetic stimulation during the acquisition of new fine motor skills. *Journal of Neurophysiology, 74(3)*, 1037-1045.

Perry, B.D., Pollard, R.A., Blakely, T.L., Baker, W.L. & Vigilante, D. (1995). Childhood trauma, the neurobiology of adaptation, and "use-dependent" development of the brain: How "states" become "traits." *Infant Mental Health Journal, 16*, 271-291.

Perry, B.D. (2000). The neuroarcheology of childhood maltreatment, the neurodevelopmental costs of adverse childhood events. In B. Geffner (Ed.), *The Cost of Child Maltreatment: Who Pays? We All Do*. Binghamton, N.Y.: Haworth Press.

Pillemer, K., Fuller-Rowell, T., Reid, M. & Wells, N. (2010). Environmental Volunteering and Health Outcomes over a 20-Year Period. *Gerontologist*, February 2010.

Raine, A., Melroy, J.R., & Bihrle, S. (1998). Reduced prefrontal and increased subcortical brain functioning assessed using positron emission tomography in predatory and affective murderers. *Behavior Science and the Law 16:* 319–32.

Restak, R.M. (2001). *The Secret Life of the Brain.* New York: Dana Press.

Rosenzweig, E.S., Barnes, C.A. & McNaughton, B.L. (2002). Making room for new memories. *Nature Neuroscience, 5(1),* 6-8.

Rubenstein, J.L. & Merzenich, M.M. (2003). Model of autism: Increased ratio of excitation/inhibition in key neural systems. *Genes, Brain and Behavior, 2,* 255-267.

Sapolsky, R.M., Romero, L.M. & Munch, A. (2000). How do glucorticoids influence stress responses? Integrating permissive, suppressive, stimulatory and preparative actions. *Endocrine Reviews, 21(1),* 55-89.

Schaffer, H. R., & Emerson, P. E. (1964). The development of social attachments in infancy. *Monographs for the Society for Research in Child Development, 29* (3, Serial No. 94).

Schore, A.N. (1994). *Affect regulation and the origin of the self: The neurobiology of emotional development.* Mahwah, NJ: Erlbaum.

Schore, A. (2001). The effects of a secure attachment relationship on right brain development, affect regulation, and Infant mental health. *Infant Mental Health Journal, 22,* 210-269.

Schore, A. (2003). *Affect Regulation and the Repair of the Self.* New York: W.W. Norton.

Shonkoff, J.P., Boyce, W.T., Cameron, J., Duncan, G.J., Fox, N.A., Gunnar, M.R., Levitt, P. McEwen, B.S., Nelson, C.A. Phillips, D. & Thompson, R.A. (2005). Excessive stress disrupts the architecture of the developing brain. http://www.developing child.net.

Siegel, D. (2003). An interpersonal neurobiology of psychotherapy. In D.J. Siegel and M. Solomon, *Healing Trauma*. New York: W.W. Norton & Company.

Siegel, D. (2010). *Mindsight*. New York: Random House.

Seligman, M. (2002). *Authentic Happiness: Using the new Positive Psychology to Realize Your Potential for Lasting Fulfillment*. New York: The Free Press.

Silberman, S. (2009). Placebos are getting more effective. Drug companies are desperate to know why. *Wired Magazine 19*(09).

Spangler, G., Schieche, M., Ilg, U., Maier, U. & Ackerman, C. (1994). Maternal sensitivity as an organizer for biobehavioral regulation in infancy. *Developmental Psychobiology, 27*, 425-437.

Sprinson, J.S. & Berrick, K. (2010). *Unconditional Care, Relationship-based Behavioral Intervention with Vulnerable Children and Families*. New York: Oxford University Press.

Sroufe, L. A., Egeland, B., Carlson, E. & Collins, W. A. (2005). Attachment and development: A prospective, longitudinal study from birth to adulthood. *Attachment and Human Development, 7*(4): 349-367.

Sroufe, L. A., Egeland, B., Carlson, E., & Collins, W. A. (2005). Placing early attachment experiences in developmental context. In K. E. Grossmann, K. Grossmann, & E. Waters (Eds.), *Attachment from infancy to adulthood: The major longitudinal studies* (pp. 48-70). New York: Guilford Publications.

Temple, E., Deutsch, G.K., Poldrack, R.A., Miller, S.L., Tallal, P., Merzenich, M.M. & Gabrieli. (2003). Neural deficits in children with dyslexia ameliorated by behavioral remediation. *Proceedings of the National Academy of Sciences, USA, 100*(5), 2860-2865.

Trevarthen, C. (1998), Explaining Emotions in Attachment. *Social Development, 7*, 269-272.

van der Kolk, B. A., McFarlane A.C. & Weisaeth, L. (Eds.) (1996). *Traumatic Stress: the effects of overwhelming experience on mind, body, and society.* New York, Guilford Press, 214-241.

van der Kolk, B.A., Perry, J.C. & Herman, J.L. (1991). Childhood origins of self-destructive behavior. *American Journal of Psychiatry.* 148, 1665-1671.

Vaughn, S.C. (1997). *The talking cure: the science behind psychotherapy.* New York: Grosset/Putnam.

Voigt, T., Baier, H., & De Lima, A.D. (1997). Synchronization of neuronal activity promotes survival of individual rat neocortical neurons in early development. *European Journal of Neuroscience 9*, 990-999.

Wagner, T.D., Rilling, J.K., Smith, E.E., Sokolik, A., Casey, K.L., Davidson, R.J., Kosslyn, S.M., Rose, R.M. & Cohen, J.D. (2004). Placebo-induced changes in fMRI in the anticipation and experience of pain. *Science 303(5661)*, 1162-1167.

Watts, A. (1960)."The Value of Psychotic Experience." http://deoxy.org/w_value.htm.

Weinstock, M. (1997). Does prenatal stress impair coping and regulation of hypothalamic-pituitary-adrenal axis? *Neuroscience and Biological Behavior Review, 21*(1), 1-10.

Weaver, I.C., Diorio, J., Seckl, J.R., Szyf, M. & Meaney, .J. (2004). Early environmental regulation of hippocampal glucocorticoid receptor gene expression: genomic target sites. *Annals of the New York Academy of Sciences, 1024*, 182-212.

Wittling, W. & Pfluger, M. (1990). Neuroendocrine hemisphere asymmetries: Salivary cortisol secretion during lateralized viewing of emotion-related and neutral films. *Brain and Cognition, 14*, 243-265.

Wittstein, I. (2007). The broken heart syndrome. *Cleveland Clinic Journal of Medicine. 7*: S17.

Young, Robert M. 1990. *Mind, Brain, and Adaptation in the Nineteenth Century: Cerebral Localization and Its Biological Context from Gall to Ferrier*. New York: Oxford University Press.

Yue, G. & Cole, K.J. (1992). Strength increases from the motor program: Comparison of training with maximal voluntary and imagined muscle contractions. *Journal of Neurophysiology, 67(5)*, 1114-1123.

Ziegler, D.L. (2000). *Raising Children Who Refuse To Be Raised, Parenting Skills and Therapy Interventions for the Most Difficult Children.* Phoenix: Acacia Publishing.

Ziegler, D.L. (2002). *Traumatic Experience and the Brain, A Handbook for Understanding and Treating Those Traumatized as Children.* Phoenix: Acacia Publishing.

Ziegler, D.L. (2008). *Beyond Healing, the Path to Personal Contentment after Trauma.* Phoenix: Acacia Publishing.

Zautra, A. J. (2003). *Emotions, Stress, and Health.* London: Oxford University Press.